C000137501

Stress Solutions for t

Stress Solutions for the Overstretched

by

David E. Gibbons and J. Tim Newton

*Dept of Dental Public Health
and Oral Health Services Research
Kings College London, Guys Hospital,
London SE1 9RT*

Series Editor
Fiona Stuart-Wilson, MA (Cantab), Assoc. IPD, MIMC CMC

Published by the British Dental Association
64 Wimpole Street, London W1M 8AL

© *British Dental Journal* 1998

All rights reserved. No part of this publication may
be reproduced, stored in a retrieval system, or transmitted
in any form or by any means, electronic,
mechanical, photocopying, recording or otherwise,
without either the permission of the publishers or a
licence permitting restricted copying in the United
Kingdom issued by the Copyright Licensing Agency Ltd,
90 Tottenham Court Road, London, W1P 9HE

ISBN 0 904 58854 8

Produced for the Publisher by
Chase Production Services, Chadlington, OX7 3LN
Printed and bound in Great Britain by
The Cromwell Press, Trowbridge

Contents

Foreword by Professor Cary L. Cooper   ix

1 **Introduction**   1

2 **So this is stress**   3
  Stimulus based models of stress   3
  Response based models of stress   5
  Interactionist models of stress   7
  What is stressful about working in dentistry   9
  Summary   12
  Further reading   12

3 **So this is what it looks and feels like:**
  The manifestations of stress   14
  The effects of stress on the person   14
  The effects of stress on working relationships   20
  Summary   21
  Further reading   22

4 **Am I stressed?**   23
  What makes me feel stressed?   23
  About my body   24
  About my thoughts   26
  About my behaviour   27
  About my health   28
  General questions   28
  Supplementary questions   29

5 **Personal re-engineering: Changing our lifestyles**   30
  Learning to relax   30
  Changing our diet   32
  Taking exercise   34
  Hobbies as stress management   34
  Identifyng social support   35
  Summary   35
  Further reading   36

6 Environmental management 37
Stress and strain on the eyes 37
Stress and strain on the ears 37
Stress and strain on the back and skeleton 38
Summary 40
Further reading 40

7 'Stop the world I want to get off':
Time management 41
Setting our time priorities 41
Becoming aware of your time 43
Managing time constraints 45
Summary 49
Further reading 50

8 Personnel management 51
Identifying the right people for your team 51
Communicating with your team 52
Effective team working 52
Addressing problems with the team 54
Handling change within the work environment 55
Summary 56
Further reading 56

9 Changing behaviour 57
Stress and health related behaviour 57
Stress and the general disruption of behaviour 59
Stress and critical incidents 61
Summary 64
Further reading 64

10 Cognitive reassessment 66
Negative thinking 66
How can we change these thoughts? 70
Critical analysis of thoughts 70
Summary 73
Further reading 73

11 Am I still stressed? 75
What makes me feel stressed? 75
About my body 76

About my thoughts   77
About my behaviour   79
About my health   79
General questions   80
Supplementary questions   81

12 Summary   82
Identify stress and its effects   82
Identify options for change and implement change   83
Reassess stress levels   83

Appendix   Useful addresses   84
Index   89

Foreword

The world of work is dramatically changing, with more short-term contracts, part-time working and a more managerialist, bottom-line attitude towards the workplace. This latter development is particularly prevalent in health care services, where budgets, through-put, performance indicators and the like now predominate, with clinical issues sometimes subjugated to business demands. These types of work-related pressures, together with the changing role of the dentist (balancing between the public and private sector), makes dentistry a high risk occupation. This book attempts to help dentists manage their ever changing world, with practical advice and support. It helps to underpin and encourage John Ruskin's belief, posited as long ago as 1851, that 'in order that people may be happy in their work, these three things are needed: they must be fit for it; they must not do too much of it; and they must have a sense of success in it'.

Professor Cary L. Cooper,
Professor of Organizational Psychology and Pro Vice Chancellor
of the University of Manchester Institute of Science and Technology

1

Introduction

It has been said that if a starving rabbit were placed equidistant between two lettuces it would die because of its inability to choose which to eat first. A similar problem of inaction can occur when *we* are overstretched or stressed. What is worse, we rarely realise that this is happening. If someone suggests to us that we are overwrought our immediate response may be denial because in our society we are led to believe that to be overstressed is to be a failure. One way in which we deny our stress is to distance ourselves from the problem, 'It's not me, rather it's the nature of the job'. But perhaps we need to think about how we manage ourselves and our time. The early starts, the late nights at work, the missed lunchtimes, the briefcase full of work that we carry to and from the surgery—all these suggest poor management of one's self. Having a full appointment book, constantly ringing telephones and other interruptions does not automatically mean you are under stress. It's not so much what happens to us that causes stress, rather how we react to it. The same experience may cause one person to want to run away and another to be excited.

The first step in dealing with stress is to identify the nature of our stress. What is it that makes us feel stressed? What effect does the stress have on our lives? How do we cope with stress? The next step is to identify what we would like our situation to be. It is easy to say that we would want a stress-free life, but what would that look like? Perhaps it would be very boring. Many of us find we are sacrificing our personal lives for the sake of our job. We are faced with the important question of do we 'work to live' or 'live to work'. What are the options for change?

This book is designed to help you with every step of the stress management process, including identifying and monitoring your personal stress levels, identifying ways to change your stress and implementing those changes. It is not designed to be read like a novel; it doesn't require you to read each chapter in turn, one after the other. Rather you should read those chapters which are most important to you. You should read Chapters 2 and 3 first: these provide you with an overview of stress and how it affects our lives. Chapter 4 will help you evaluate your personal stress level and sources of stress and it will also help to target areas which you should address in your stress management. Chapters 5 to 10 outline specific stress management strategies for particular sources of stress. Treat these chapters as individual modules which you can take in any order, missing out any which you don't feel are relevant to you at the current time. Managing your stress is an ongoing process because our stress is constantly changing as we are faced with new challenges. It is important to take the time to reassess your stress levels at regular intervals: Chapter 11 provides you with the tools to do this. Each chapter provides you with a summary of that chapter and a list of further reading.

The dental profession has been identified as potentially very stressful, but it can also be a challenging and rewarding career. This book seeks to minimise the stress and maximise the reward. If this interests you, read on …

2

So this is stress

In this chapter we will be examining definitions and models of stress. This will help us to understand what makes a situation stressful. This will be useful in later chapters when we come to examine how to cope with stress.

Stimulus based models of stress

The first group of models of stress which we can identify are called stimulus based models. They all share the characteristic that they view stress as a force (or stimulus) which acts on the person. The parallel is with the use of the term 'stress' in engineering. This makes intuitive sense; most of us when we think about being stressed imagine a situation when we are faced with too much to do, in too short a time, so that we can almost feel the weight of pressure. Figure 2.1 illustrates this type of model, where 'stress' is a force acting upon a body. Up to a point the body can bend and

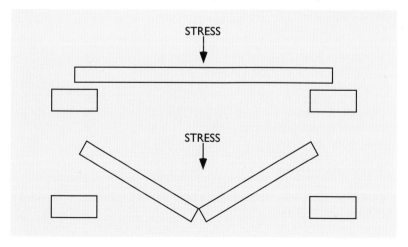

Fig. 2.1 A stimulus based model of stress

3

EVENT	LIFE CHANGE SCORE
Death of spouse	100
Divorce	73
Marital separation	65
Jail term	63
Death of close family member	63
Personal injury or illness	53
Marriage	50
Fired from job	47
Marital reconciliation	45
Retirement	45
Change in health of family member	44
Pregnancy	40
Sex problems	39
Gain of new family member	39
Business readjustment	39
Change in financial state	38
Death of a close friend	37
Change to a different line of work	36
Change in number of arguments with spouse	35
Large mortgage	31
Foreclosure of loan	30
Change in responsibilities at work	29
Son or daughter leaving home	29
Trouble with in-laws	29
Outstanding personal achievement	28
Spouse begins or stops work	26
Begin or end school	26
Change in living conditions	25
Revision of personal habits	24
Trouble with boss	23
Change in hours or conditions of work	20
Change in residence	20
Change of school	20
Change of recreation	19
Change in social activities	18
Small mortgage	17
Change in sleeping habits	16
Change in eating habits	15
Holiday	13
Christmas	12
Minor violations of law	11

Fig. 2.2   The Holmes and Rahe Schedule of Recent Events

adjust to the force, but a point is reached when the force becomes too great and the body breaks or shows signs of wear.

This type of model has been useful for understanding the effects of major events upon those people who are involved in them. There have been many such major catastrophes which have had a profound impact upon the people involved in them, their relatives and friends (for example, plane crashes, earthquakes, hurricanes).

On an individual level, there are major events which happen to us and which are highly stressful, for example, the loss of a partner, personal injury, loss of job etc. There is extensive evidence to suggest that individuals who experience a high number of such events over a period of time are more likely to suffer a variety of physical and psychological illnesses. Psychologists have developed scales which assess the level of stress experienced by people. The Schedule of Recent Events (SRE, Holmes and Rahe) asks people to indicate which of a list of events they have experienced in the previous twelve months (see Figure 2.2). Each event is given a weighting from 0 to 100 depending upon the extent to which Holmes and Rahe estimate that the event will have an impact upon the individual's life. Death of spouse is given the highest rating at 100, marriage is defined as the mid-point of the scale at 50. Note that the list includes both events which are negative (marital separation, death of a close family member) and those which are positive (marriage, holiday). This is because even events which are positive can result in a change to the way in which the individual lives his or her life.

A stimulus based model of stress does not explain everything we know and experience about stress. We know that people differ in their response to the same situation (stimulus) and that this difference cannot be understood simply in terms of what the event means to them. This is particularly true for the more minor everyday events, the stresses and hassles which we all experience.

Response based models of stress

Whenever we are faced with stress, the body undergoes a range of physiological changes. The most obvious of these is the 'fight-or-flight' response to acute stress, which results in you feeling that your heart is racing and your hands are sweaty. These physiological responses are discussed more in the next chapter. Long term stress results in chronic changes in physiology. This has led physiologists and psychologists to focus on stress as a response, that is 'stress' is defined as the production of a specific response. Any stimulus which produces a 'stress response' must be a stressor. These responses are not only physiological, there are also changes in behaviour and thoughts which happen when we are stressed (these are discussed further in Chapter 3).

The most widely known example of a response based model of stress is Selye's General Adaptation Syndrome. This model proposes a three-stage response to stress:

1. Alarm   The 'fight or flight' response.
2. Adaptation   Mechanisms are adopted to enable the individual to cope better with the ongoing stress. For example, release of corticosteroids.
3. Exhaustion   The mechanisms adopted in the Adaptation phase are no longer sufficient to allow coping in the face of ongoing stress. The consequence is 'diseases of adaptation'. The resources used in coping are depleted resulting in breakdown of physiological and psychological mechanisms.

This is illustrated in Figure 2.3. The theory applies equally well to behaviour. When stress is acute, we may introduce minor changes to cope with the stress—working longer hours, new work systems and so on. However if pressure continues then these changes are not sufficient to continue coping with the stress.

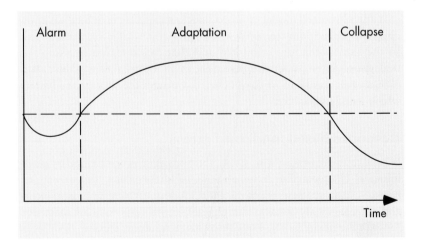

Fig. 2.3   Selye's General Adaptation Syndrome

Interactionist models of stress

Interactionist models of stress combine the stimulus based models and the response based models. Stress is defined as a mismatch between demand and ability to meet that demand. When this mismatch occurs it gives rise to physiological, cognitive and behavioural consequences. Cox (1978) has outlined an interactionist model of stress (see Figure 2.4).

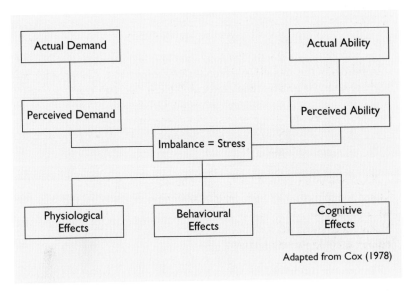

Adapted from Cox (1978)

Fig. 2.4   Cox's Interactionist model of stress

Put simply, this model suggests that we interpret stress as an imbalance between demands and ability. Where demand and ability are in balance, there is no stress.

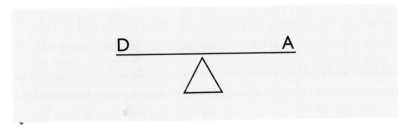

Fig. 2.5   Demand and Ability in balance

But when demand exceeds ability, we will begin to experience stress.

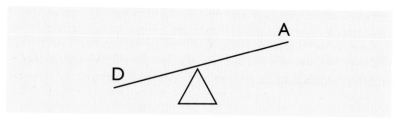

Fig. 2.6   Demand exceeds Ability

Importantly, this model also predicts that the reverse is also stressful, that is where ability is greater than demand. We call this 'rust out'.

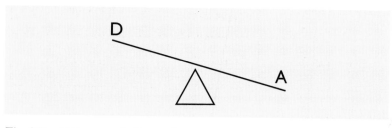

Fig. 2.7   Ability exceeds Demand

This simple model tells us when a situation will be stressful. However, this model is not complete. We need to add some more information in order to make it fit all the observed facts about stress. These concern: perceptions, uncontrollability and unpredictability.

Although we have defined stress as a mismatch between demand and ability, the absolute levels of demand and ability are less important than the *perceptions* of them. We can probably all recall people whom we know who have very little confidence in their own abilities—their perceived ability is low, much lower than their actual ability. Similarly we possibly also know people who have a very high level of perceived ability! Likewise perceived demand can bear little relationship to the actual demand faced by an individual, indeed it may be one of the consequences of feeling stressed that we begin to think that the demand we face is far greater than it actually is—this is called 'magnification' and is a common consequence of negative thinking.

Not all demands are equally stressful. Generally we find stress that is unpredictable and uncontrollable more stressful than stress which is not so. When events and challenges are predictable and controllable, then we may find them a challenge or we may find them to be dull. More exciting, and more challenging, are situations that we can exercise some control over but which are unpredictable, for example skiing down an unfamiliar run (we choose to do this activity and can choose to stop, but it is new and unfamiliar). Also exciting and challenging are activities which are uncontrollable but predictable—we can say with a fair degree of certainty what will happen and when it will happen. This is summarised in Figure 2.8.

Nature of stress	Controllable	Uncontrollable
Predictable	May be challenging, may be boring	Challenge
Unpredictable	Challenge	Highly stressful

Fig. 2.8 The nature of stress

What is stressful about working in dentistry?

A number of studies have identified the aspects of working in the dental profession that are most stressful. Most of this research has looked only at the dentists and their experience of stress, although there are a few studies which have examined the stress levels of other professionals working in the dental setting. We will start by looking at stress in dental nurses.

Sources of stress—dental nurses

Blinkhorn and his colleagues carried out a series of interviews with dental nurses and found that the most commonly listed sources of stress for this group are as shown in Figure 2.9.

Similar findings have been reported by other researchers. From this list we can identify that many of the factors are beyond the control of the dental nurse. The amount of money that the dental nurse earns is largely under the control of the employer: a common complaint about working hours is that they are determined by the dentist—if he or she chooses to stay behind to finish a patient then it is 'expected' that the support staff

- Worry about earning enough money
- Being blamed for mistakes
- Long working hours
- Being behind schedule
- Dealing with money
- Feeling undervalued in the dental team
- Difficult patients

Fig. 2.9   Commonly listed sources of stress for dental nurses

stay as well. The dentist is earning money by doing this—the dental nurse isn't. There is also a feeling that the dental nurse is given responsibility without control over the situation—being blamed for mistakes, dealing with money, feeling undervalued, and being behind schedule.

Take some time to consider the stress faced by dental nurses. In your experience, is the list above accurate? What would you add to the list?

Sources of stress—hygienists

Hygienists often work on a part-time basis in one or more practice. They are often self-employed and may have patients booked on their behalf. The three sources of stress identified for hygienists are shown in Figure 2.10.

- Feeling an 'outsider' in the practice
- Prevention (and therefore an important part of the hygienist's role) being undervalued by dentists
- Patient appointments being booked too closely together, so time management is made difficult

Fig. 2.10   Sources of stress identified for hygenists

Because of the part-time nature of many hygienists' work, they may not be included in staff meetings or informal staff talks and discussions. They may, therefore, not feel part of the team. It is important when considering the development of teams and the stress management of all personnel, to remember the needs of part-time staff. We will consider this further in Chapter 8.

Uncontrollability and unpredictability again emerge as factors which influence our stress experience. The experience of having somebody else schedule your patients and not being able to control your own appointment book is likely to lead to the perception that demand is uncontrollable and unpredictable.

If you are a hygienist, or there is a hygienist in your practice, consider your (or their) stress levels. How many of the stressors listed here apply to you (or your colleague)?

Sources of stress—dentists

Some quotes from our interviews with dentists in NHS practices will illustrate their sources of stress:

We're not trained as businessmen, we're trained as dentists. And yet we are now businessmen and it's a question of trying to get the right balance, the right compromise between doing the dentistry and getting the right turnover.

Difficult patients, that stresses me, obviously. Nervous patients in particular … they get me edgy and I find it rubs off more these days than it used to when I was younger.

The largest survey of the stress experienced by general dental practitioners was carried out by Cooper and his colleagues in 1987. They identified five major sources of stress. Similar results have been found by other researchers using a wide variety of research methods. The most commonly cited sources of stress in dental practices are shown in Figure 2.11.

An update on this survey, carried out by Waddington (1997), found that in the ten years since the previous survey a number of new stressors have arisen (see Figure 2.12 overleaf).

Many of these sources of stress are familiar to us: the increasing demands placed upon us by the expectations of patients, the need to carry out a certain amount of treatment in order to earn sufficient money,

- Time and scheduling pressures
- Pay related stressors
- Patients' unfavourable perceptions of dentists
- Staff and technical problems
- Dealing with patients

Fig. 2.11 Commonly cited sources of stress in dental practices

- Changes in the funding of NHS dentistry
- High patient expectations
- Staff turnover
- Financial worries
- Increasing numbers of patients

Fig. 2.12 Some new stressors identified by Waddington (1997)

the pressures of running a small business. For many of these demands, most notably the business aspects, we have little or no formal training.

We will be examining all these sources of stress and others in later chapters, where we also explore techniques for addressing the harmful effects such stress may have upon all of us. The next chapter addresses some of the effects of stress, and in Chapter 4 we ask you to look at your personal stress levels, as part of which we will ask you to examine those characteristics of your work which you find stressful.

Summary

Stress results from a mismatch between the *demand* placed upon you as a person, and your *ability* to meet that demand. It arises from your perceptions of demand and ability, and your perception of the mismatch. Some demands are more stressful than others, in particular demands which are *unpredictable* and *uncontrollable*.

Stress results in many responses which include changes in your *physiology*, your *thoughts* and your *behaviour*.

The demands faced by members of the dental team differ slightly across different professions, but there are some common stressors, in particular 'difficult' patients, worries about money and working long hours.

Further reading

Two general textbooks on stress which describe the theoretical models of stress and some of the research examining the effects of stress.

Cooper, C.L., Cooper, R.D. and Eaker, L.H. (1988) *Living with Stress*. London: Penguin.
Cox, T. (1978) *Stress*. London: Macmillan.

Six papers which look at the stress of working as a health care professional. The papers look at different groups of health care professionals using a range of different methods.

Cooper, C.L., Watts, J. and Kelly, M. 'Job satisfaction, mental health and job stressors among general dental practitioners in the UK.' *British Dental Journal*, **24**: 77–88. (1987).

Kent, G. 'Stress amongst dentists.' In Payne, R. and Firth-Cozens, J. (eds) *Stress and Health Professionals*. London: J Wiley & Sons (1987).

Blinkhorn, A.S. 'Stress and the dental team: A qualitative investigation of the causes of stress in general practice.' *Dental Update*, **19**: 385–7 (1992).

Humphris, G.M. and Peacock, L. 'Occupational stress and job satisfaction in the community dental service of north Wales: A pilot study.' *Community Dental Health*, **10**: 73–82 (1992).

Newton, J.T. and Gibbons, D.E. 'Stress in dental practice: A qualitative comparison of dentists working within the NHS and those working within an independent capitation scheme.' *British Dental Journal*, **180**: 329–34 (1996).

Waddington, T.J. 'New stressors for GDPs in the past 10 years'. *British Dental Journal*, **182**: 82–3 (1997).

3

So this is what it looks and feels like: The manifestations of stress

In the previous chapter we looked at models of stress and discussed how stress causes physiological changes to occur in our bodies. In this chapter we will share some of the ways in which stress at work can express itself in the way in which we think and behave. First we will examine the personal manifestations of stress, that is the way in which stress affects us as people including our physical status, our thoughts and our behaviour. In the second part of the chapter we will look at how stress at work influences the way in which people work together.

The effects of stress on the person

Stress affects four aspects of us as people:

1 Our physiology
2 Our thoughts
3 Our behaviour
4 Our health

Physiological changes

The physiological effects of stress can be sub-divided into two types: *acute* and *chronic*. When we are faced with immediate stress which is short lived the body reacts with many physiological changes which help us cope. These *acute* responses are usually short lived and can be very helpful; they have been called the flight–fight response. These short-term changes are mediated by the autonomic nervous system (ANS) through the release of adrenaline. They are described in Figure 3.1.

These physiological changes give rise to the signs and symptoms we associate with feeling nervous or stressed, for example the 'butterflies in the stomach' we experience before an important examination, nausea, sweaty palms, a feeling that your heart is racing when really frightened.

- Increased heart rate
- Increased rate of perspiration
- Blood is diverted from the stomach and stomach motility declines
- Blood is sent to the muscles and periphery
- Pupils of the eyes widen

Fig. 3.1   Acute physiological responses to stress

These signs and symptoms are usually short lived and self-limiting. Limited exposure to the acute stress reaction is not likely to be a problem, and may actually be beneficial (many people engage in sports and hobbies which create this response). If you find that you are constantly experiencing these symptoms then you may want to think about reducing the stress in your daily life. There are several steps you can take including: restructuring your work; relaxation training; taking regular exercise; reducing caffeine intake. These are discussed in greater detail in Chapter 5.

If stress continues for a prolonged period (that is it becomes *chronic*) a different set of physiological responses occur. Adrenaline is no longer released into the blood stream, but instead a number of substances, called corticosteroids, are released. These are normally associated with being released to help the body fight disease, but they are also released to help in long-term coping with the physiological demands of stress. As a result, blood levels of corticosteroids are often used as a way of measuring long-term stress. However, high blood levels of corticosteroids are also related to increased health risks, particularly heart problems. Furthermore, our body can only continue to release corticosteroids for a limited amount of time, after which our body becomes depleted and the physiological response collapses. We previously referred to this breakdown in long-term adaptation when describing Selye's General Adaptation Syndrome in Chapter 2. Thus, the body's short-term response to stress is usually beneficial but if chronic stress recurs there are detrimental effects on our overall health and the way which we perceive ourselves, those around us and our situations.

Changes in thoughts

Stress, particularly chronic stress, is associated with changes in thought processes. Generally these changes can be viewed as a move towards thinking more negatively about ourselves and our situation. A summary

- Poor concentration
- Memory loss
- Intrusive negative thoughts
- Magnification of issues
- Catastrophising
- Rumination

Fig. 3.2   Changes in thoughts associated with stress

of some of the negative thoughts associated with stress is given in Figure 3.2.

Poor concentration and memory loss are relatively mild symptoms of stress which may act as early warning signs that our stress levels are beginning to have an effect upon our life. Often these are not seen as the early indicators they can be. We shrug them off as being associated with age or a particularly busy time—where busy in our minds does not equate with stressful. These signs can relatively easily remit, for example if we have a holiday or take some other sort of break. However, as stress becomes more chronic then concentration and memory can become worse, requiring a more systematic approach to changing our stress experience.

Intrusive negative thoughts are those we feel unable to control and where the content of the thoughts is related to expectations of failure or catastrophic outcomes. These thoughts are particularly distressing because we perceive ourselves as having little or no control over the occurrence or content of the thoughts. Examples may include,

I didn't do my best with that patient. I could have done a much better treatment if I spent more time on it.

My patients think I'm a terrible dentist.

I'm not treating the patients quickly enough.

The other staff all despise me.

These intrusive thoughts typically have three main characteristics—they are:

- Negative
- Global (they encompass everybody or all situations)
- Stable (they are thought to reflect a permanent situation)

Taking the examples above we can see these characteristics. The statement 'My patients think I'm a terrible dentist' is *negative* ('terrible'), it is *global* (the statement includes all patients) and it is *stable* (there is an implication that this is a permanent truth and reflects some fixed characteristic of ourselves).

In Chapter 10 we talk more about negative thinking and look at ways in which we can change these thinking patterns. As an example here we will be looking at three specific types of negative thinking: *magnification, catastrophising* and *rumination*.

When you feel stressed, minor events and occurrences which would otherwise be of little significance can take on the status of a major problem in your mind. We call this *magnification*. For example, in discussing stress with general dental practitioners we found that many report that they have spent hours worrying about a particular patient, whom they see as being 'difficult'. A quote from one of the dentists we interviewed will illustrate this:

> *I used to look in the appointment book the night before, you know, just to see what kind of thing I'd be doing. And if I saw this one name, Patient A I'll call her, well that would be it, I'd be awake all night thinking about Patient A, about whether she'd be happy with her denture and whether she would kick up a fuss.*

This quote also illustrates another type of negative thinking, *catastrophising*, that is where we can only imagine the worst happening. The dentist in the quote can only imagine that Patient A will be upset and unhappy with her denture. He is already worrying that he is going to have to make adjustments for her and deal with her moans and complaints, which will mean running late for the next patient, more stress, time pressures etc. Such thoughts have a tendency to become self-fulfilling: as we get more and more anxious about the forthcoming event our behaviour changes, perhaps we are less friendly towards the patient than we normally would be, or we are on our guard against anything they might say. No wonder then that the patient isn't very friendly towards us.

Finally there is an element of *rumination* to this quote. The dentist says that he spends a long time thinking about the patient's appointment, probably a lot more time than it warrants. Rumination refers to a type of thinking where the person thinks about one particular problem or situation for long periods of time and in a very narrow, usually negative way. Thinking in this way is unlikely to produce solutions to the problem.

What else could this dentist have thought? First of all, is it likely to be as big a problem as he is now making it appear? There isn't actually much evidence of what will happen. Until Patient A actually arrives at her appointment we don't know what she's going to say. Secondly, by knowing what is likely to happen we can take steps to minimise the consequences. Patient A might need a little more time than she has been allocated, so the dentist in this example could go to work the next morning and ask the reception staff to inform subsequent patients that there may be a small delay, taking the pressure off catching up with time. Also he could rehearse what he wants to say to Patient A—if she has concerns perhaps she should book a longer appointment towards the end of a day, say in the next week.

Although this is only one example, we hope it illustrates the difference between taking a situation and thinking only negatively about it, and taking the same situation and putting it into a more positive framework. This is discussed further in Chapter 10.

Changes in Behaviour

Our behaviour changes when we are feeling stressed. These changes are widespread and can vary greatly in their extent both for different people and for the same person at different points in time. Some of the changes in behaviour that are associated with stress are listed below (Figure 3.3)

- Increased smoking
- Increased alcohol consumption
- Change in diet
- Decreased repertoire of coping behaviours
- Social withdrawal

Fig. 3.3   Behavioural signs of stress

Both acute and chronic stress can have very profound effects on behaviour. Many of these will be familiar to us and are widely acknowledged, for example changes in diet, smoking and drinking. More subtle changes, which we often don't notice, include social withdrawal and a decreased repertoire of coping behaviours.

When we are experiencing severe stress we may withdraw from friends and spend more time on our own. This may be because we feel unable to cope with the perceived demand that others may make on us or because we feel embarrassed or ashamed that we are not coping well. Of course, such withdrawal is not always helpful. Indeed having friends and colleagues with whom you can discuss problems and difficulties, as well as possible solutions, is invaluable in helping us to deal with our stress. At work, too, we withdraw from interacting with colleagues when we are experiencing stress.

Withdrawal from social interaction is one specific example of a more general change in behaviour under stress, that is the reduction of the range of behaviours in which we engage. This is usually described as an increasing rigidity of behaviour, decreasing flexibility and a tendency to persevere in a narrow, pre-existing behaviour pattern. It is not unusual for us when we are under stress from too much work to attempt to 'cope' by spending more time at work, working longer hours, taking fewer breaks— all behaviours which continue the pre-existing pattern which has led to there being too much work in the first place. Instead of thinking in a broader sense about the demands and events which have created our stress, we focus on trying to be more 'efficient' in coping with the existing demands. In Chapter 2 we described stress as a mismatch between demand and ability. All too often we try to cope with stress by only changing one side of this balance.

Changes in health

A number of changes in health have been associated with acute and chronic stress levels. Some of these are summarised in Figure 3.4.

Physical	Psychological
• Asthma	• Low self esteem
• Amenorrhoea	• Depression
• Coronary Heart Disease	• Anxiety
• Headaches and Migraine	• Insomnia
• Diabetes Mellitus	• Fatigue
• Ulcers	

Fig. 3.4 Changes in health

We are very familiar with the idea of stress-induced illness. In fact it seems that stress is related to almost every illness that affects us. There are two possible mechanisms for this. First, as we have described, stress has profound effects on the body's physiology, including producing changes in the body's immune system. It seems possible then that there is a direct action of stress upon the body's susceptibility to disease. Low grade infections such as colds and flu may be more common in people under stress, who have depleted their body's natural immune coping response. Headaches and migraine may be related to increased muscle tension associated with stress. Heart disease is probably related to increased risk of blocked arteries as a result of increased blood levels of free fatty acids resulting from the increased mobilisation of corticosteroids.

The second mechanism by which stress may produce illness is indirectly through behaviour. Stress produces many changes in behaviour, including changes in diet, exercise, tobacco and alcohol use. But there are also more subtle effects. Where time pressures are great, it is quicker and easier to work with direct vision and many dentists report adopting awkward postures in order to get direct vision. Is it any wonder then that back problems are so common among the dental community?

Low self-esteem, anxiety and depression are signs that stress is having a profound effect upon our everyday functioning. If you are experiencing these kinds of symptoms, then it is likely that you are experiencing high levels of stress and you should take action very quickly.

The effects of stress on working relationships

The dental team is composed of many personnel, and would include in its broadest terms: dentists, dental nurses, hygienists, therapists, receptionists, practice managers, administrative support staff, cleaning staff and technical support staff. In order to provide high quality patient care all these colleagues have to work smoothly together and communicate effectively. Even if some members of the 'team' are not directly employed within the practice, it is still important that they receive and provide timely information efficiently and effectively. Let us look at some of the important issues concerning stress and teamwork.

1. Communications

When a group of people are under stress, it is not unusual for their communications to become less effective. There may be a shift from open and honest communications to rushed communications, where important information is forgotten or not mentioned. It is a common assumption that effective communication takes time—we tend to think that talking to someone, explaining what we mean and seeking their views on a matter is a time-consuming process. When we are under stress it seems quicker and more efficient to rush through things, making our own decisions and not consulting others. Some people even adopt this attitude to their own stress, 'I'm too busy to talk about what's stressing me!'

2. Motivation for work

Stress decreases our motivation to work. When going to work is an unpleasant experience associated with negative thoughts, a range of physiological symptoms and poor health, it is perfectly reasonable to dread the experience. Low motivation among staff has many consequences for their behaviour—ranging from absence and leaving the job to more subtle effects such as a general lack of concern for patients and other colleagues.

3. Staff absence and turnover

High rates of staff sickness and turnover are likely to reflect a situation where staff feel undervalued and overstressed. Dental nurses are a group who have very high turnover rates. As we saw in Chapter 2, common sources of stress for this group are a feeling of being undervalued, and being blamed for everyone's mistakes.

4. Role ambiguity

Lack of communication and an atmosphere of high stress can lead to a lack of clarity in the role of colleagues. It is not uncommon for role ambiguity to lead to conflict between team members regarding their responsibilities and duties, especially where colleagues may perceive some competition between each other. For example, within your practice is it clear who should tidy the waiting area, who should wash up the staff coffee cups, who stays late when? These little issues can lead to festering disputes as colleagues begin to feel unsupported and undervalued.

Summary

Stress has profound effects on you as an individual and those around you. These are summarised in the figure below.

In the next chapter we have provided a series of questionnaires for you to assess your stress levels, based on these manifestations of stress. The questionnaires will help you identify how stress affects you and refer you to later chapters which will help you with your specific stress-related matters.

	Acute	Chronic
Changes in Physiology	Fight/Flight response	Decline in immune response Exhaustion Elevated blood corticosteroid levels
Changes in Thoughts	Poor concentration Memory loss	Increasingly negative appraisal of self and life
Changes in Behaviour	Disruption of usual behaviour	Narrowing of behavioural repertoire Social withdrawal
Changes in Health	Fatigue Headaches	Increasing risk of major illness Coronary Heart Disease Ulcers Depression Anxiety
Changes in Team Relationships	Poor communication Decline in work motivation Increased staff absence and turnover Lack of clarity in team roles	

Fig. 3.5 Summary of the manifestations of stress

Further reading

An excellent introduction to the topic of stress and its effects.

Cooper, C.L., Cooper, R.D. and Eaker, L.H. (1988) *Living with Stress*. London: Penguin.

A good description of how stress has a wide-ranging impact upon our lives, including work, home life and health.

Cox, T. (1982) *Stress*. London: Macmillan.

A description of stress in the dental profession, summarising much of the research in this area.

Kent, G. 'Stress amongst dentists.' In Payne, R. and Firth-Cozens, J. (eds) *Stress and Health Professionals*. London: J Wiley & Sons, (1987)

4

Am I stressed?

In this chapter we have given you a set of questionnaires for you to complete. They are a stress audit, and are designed to assess how much stress you are experiencing. This information will then allow you to plan how to change the levels of stress that you are experiencing. Techniques for changing your stress are listed in Chapters 5 to 10. The type of change that you make will depend in part on your answers to these questions.

What makes me feel stressed?

Make a list of everything in your work life that gives you the feeling of being stressed. You might want to draw on the examples we gave you in Chapter 2, and see whether those apply to you personally.

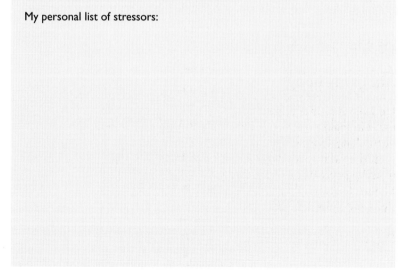

My personal list of stressors:

Fig. 4.1a Personal list of stressors

23

Now, look at your list and decide which is the most important, the biggest stressor on your list. Put a 1 next to that. Then decide which is the second biggest stressor and put a 2 next to that. Continue until you have the 'top five' sources of your personal stress. Put them in the table below.

Re-examine your list and decide which of these you think will be the easiest to change. Place a 1 in the 'Ease of Change' column next to this one. Again rank each stress in terms of how easy it is to change. These priorities can help you to pick which chapter you will read first. The questions which follow will also help you to focus on which of the readings and exercises you should start with.

My personal TOP FIVE sources of stress

Importance Rank	Stress	Ease of Change
1		
2		
3		
4		
5		

Fig. 4.1b   Top five sources of stress

About my body

How often in an average week do you experience the signs and symptoms listed in Figure 4.2 at any time when you are travelling to work, at work, or thinking about work?

Add up the score that you have given yourself. A score of 8 or more would suggest that you are having some marked symptoms of stress very frequently. A score of 12 or more suggests a very high level of physiological signs and symptoms of stress.

If your score is 7 or below: You do not have many physiological signs and symptoms at this time. You should complete the other sections of this assessment, since it is possible that your personal stress is manifest in a different way. Ask those who work with you, and your close friends and family, whether they think you are experiencing stress. It may be that you simply have not noticed the signs.

If your score is between 8 and 11:

You have distressing physiological signs and symptoms of stress. Chapters 5 and 10 will help you to identify ways to address these symptoms.

If your score is 12 or more:

This is a very high level of physiological symptoms, suggesting that you are having some signs at least twice a week, and possibly more often than this. Start with Chapter 5 and work through to looking at what makes your work environment so stressful (Chapter 6).

	Once a day or more (Score 3)	2–3 times a week (Score 2)	Once a week or less (Score 1)
Feeling that your heart is pounding			
Feeling that your pulse is racing			
Excessively sweaty hands			
'Butterflies' in the stomach			
Feeling that you are having difficulty breathing			
Feelings of muscle tension			
My total is: _____ Date: _____			

Fig. 4.2 Physiological signs and symptoms of stress

	Once a day or more (Score 3)	2–3 times a week (Score 2)	Once a week or less (Score 1)
Having difficulty concentrating			
Forgetting things, particularly little details			
Worrying about mistakes that you have made			
Worrying about what patients think of you			
Worrying about what your colleagues think of you			
Going over and over in your mind things that happened at work			
Having difficulty making decisions			
Losing confidence in yourself *			
Thinking of yourself as worthless *			
Feeling unhappy and depressed *			

* Score yourself double on these items

My total is: _____   Date: _____

Fig. 4.3   Cognitive signs and symptoms of stress

About my thoughts

How often do you find yourself experiencing the thoughts listed in Figure 4.3?

Add up your score on the items (remembering to double your score on some items).

If your score is 15 or less: Your score is low. You rarely think negatively about your work situation. This is good. You should continue completing the questionnaires in this section, in case your stress is manifest in a different way.

If your score is between 16 and 25:	You experience quite a number of negative thoughts in relation to work. You should certainly consider reading Chapter 10 to identify how you might take a more positive attitude towards work and your work stress.
If your score is 26 or more:	You frequently think negatively about your work. You are probably approaching the limits of your stress. This high score is particularly concerning if you have indicated a very frequent response for the items marked with an asterisk. You should read Chapter 10 as a priority.

About my behaviour

Over the last six months have you noticed any of the following changes in behaviour?

	✓ or x
Smoking more	
Drinking more alcohol	
Changes in diet (eating more, eating less)	
Seeing less of friends	
Taking sick leave from work	
Having more arguments with colleagues	
Working late more often	
Missing more lunch breaks	
Number of changes identified: _____ Date: _____	

Fig. 4.4   Behavioural signs and symptoms of stress

If you have noticed any of the changes in behaviour listed above then we would advise you to read Chapter 9, which examines the effects of stress on behaviour, and Chapter 5, which will help you to find other ways of dealing with the effects of stress. The more of these changes that you have ticked, the more priority you should give to reading and working through Chapter 9.

About my health

Over the last six months which of the following aspects of your health have changed?

	✓ or x
Feelings of tiredness and fatigue	
Increased number of headaches and migraines	
Increased number of colds	
Increasing indigestion	
Feelings of low self-esteem	
Feeling anxious	
Feeling depressed	
Number of changes identified: _____ Date: _____	

Fig. 4.5   Effects of stress on health

The changes in health noted above are all to be taken seriously. If you are experiencing any of these changes we advise you to discuss them with a General Medical Practitioner. Another good source of help is Chapter 5, which will help you to identify ways to relax and take your mind off stress. Chapter 6 will help to identify any aspects of your physical environment which may be unhealthy. Chapters 7, 9 and 10 will all help you to identify new ways of dealing with your stress.

General questions

Overall how would you rate the level of stress that you are experiencing?
(Please circle one answer)

Low						High
1	2	3	4	5	6	7

How much do you want to change this level?
(Please circle one answer)

Not at all						Very high priority
1	2	3	4	5	6	7

Fig. 4.6   General questions

It is important that you consider your own willingness to change. If this is low then any help that is offered is likely to be unsuccessful.

Supplementary questions

These questions are about how the stress you are experiencing affects those around you. They are for friends and colleagues to complete.

The perspectives of other people can be a useful guide to help you to decide to change your stress levels. Often our stress does not affect us but has quite a major impact on those around us. Compare your own willingness to change with how much those around you would like you to change your stress.

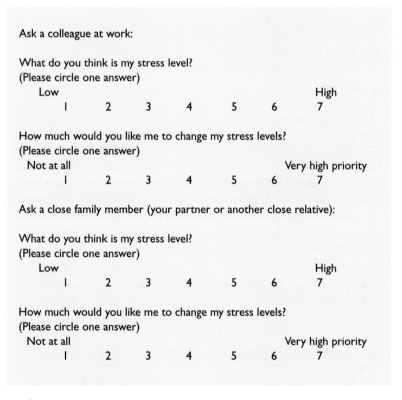

Fig. 4.7 Supplementary questions

5

Personal re-engineering: Changing our lifestyles

In this chapter we will be examining some of the ways in which we can change our lifestyles in order to reduce stress levels. In particular we will be examining five areas:

1 Learning to relax
2 Changing our diet
3 Taking exercise
4 Hobbies as stress management
5 Identifying social support

Learning to relax

As we saw in Chapter 3, stress has profound effects on our bodies. These changes are all designed to increase levels of arousal: increased heart rate, widening of the pupils, release of adrenaline and so on. This increased arousal is stressful for our bodies. *Relaxation training* employs a range of techniques designed to help reduce these levels of arousal. Calming the body is in itself beneficial, but also has a calming effect on the mind and will help to reduce the harmful effects on thoughts.

There are many different types of relaxation technique. Most involve some element of progressive muscular relaxation. In this technique muscle groups are tensed and relaxed in turn. The idea is that we learn to distinguish between a state of tension, and a state of relaxation. Having learnt this, it is easier to recognise when we are tense and so relax. The principles of progressive muscular relaxation are easily learnt, but you may find that it takes a little practice before you learn to relax completely using this method. Figure 5.1 gives instructions for progressive muscular relaxation.

Find a quiet place to relax in. The room should be warm and comfortable. When you are first learning to relax, it is usually easiest to start when you are lying down, so a bedroom may be a good place. Set aside about half an hour for your relaxation. Your clothes should be loose: avoid anything that is tight at the neck or waist. Take off your shoes.

Lie down on your back with your arms at your side and your legs out straight. Close your eyes. Concentrate on your breathing. Keep your breathing regular, deep and slow. Breathe in to a slow count of three and out to a count of three. Next concentrate on your toes. Scrunch them up so that they are tense and hold for a count of three, then relax them. Notice the difference between the feeling of your toes when they are relaxed and the feeling when they are tense. Repeat the tensing of your toes, hold the tension, and relax. Next tense your ankles and calves, hold the tension for a count of three and then relax. Again, notice the difference between tension and relaxation. Continue this process of tensing and relaxing muscle groups throughout your body moving upwards towards your head. In order, tense and relax:

Your thighs
Your buttocks
Your stomach muscles
Your shoulders
Your upper arms
Your lower arms and hands
Your neck muscles
Your facial muscles

At each stage, it is important to learn to notice the difference between the feeling of tension and the feeling of relaxation.

When you have completed the process of successively tensing and relaxing each muscle group, lie for a moment feeling the sensation of relaxation throughout your whole body. Stand up slowly and take a few moments to ease yourself into your usual routine.

With time you will come to be able to induce a state of relaxation in your muscle groups without going through the procedure of tensing the muscles. You may start to notice during the day that you are becoming tense and can just ease the muscle tension where you are sitting or standing.

Fig. 5.1   Progressive muscular relaxation

As we have mentioned previously, there are many different types of relaxation technique. You may find that some of them do not suit you. Do not let this put you off. Our experience of working with people who use relaxation techniques shows that people differ in their preferences and that most people can usually find a technique that suits them.

Barriers to using relaxation techniques are:

- 'It takes time.'   TRUE. Learning to relax takes quite a bit of time, especially at first when we are learning the technique. However with practice you will find that you become relaxed much more quickly. Also it is important that, as part of dealing with our stress overall, we learn to manage our time more effectively (see also Chapter 7).

- 'It is difficult to learn.' YES IT IS. Learning to relax is difficult, because we are trying to learn to notice how it feels to be tense, and we are not accustomed to noticing how this feels. However, after a while, if you persist, you will find that it becomes easier, and is very beneficial.

Changing our diet

Changing our diet can help to combat stress in two ways. First, when we are stressed and short of time our diet tends to move towards convenience foods which generally are high fat, high sugar and high salt. Second, a high intake of caffeine is associated with a very bad response to stress.

General diet

The key points to note about making sure that your diet is generally very healthy are:

- Eat regular meals
- Sit down to eat
- Ensure that you get a healthy balance of foods
- Avoid high-fat foods, high-salt foods and high-sugar foods

It is difficult when time is short and we are feeling pressured to take the time to sit down regularly to eat. But eating regularly throughout the day is generally better for our health than eating large amounts either at the end or the start of the day. Going for long periods of time during the day without food increases our likelihood of experiencing distressing symptoms such as heartburn, indigestion, faintness, headaches, moodiness, and probably a whole range of symptoms which we identify for ourselves as symptoms of low blood sugar. Furthermore, eating regularly throughout the day raises the Basal Metabolic Rate. This means that we are more likely to gain weight if we eat our daily calories in one big meal, rather than if we eat the same number of calories in three smaller meals evenly spaced throughout the day.

Remembering to sit down when you eat is a good way to ensure that you relax. Eating is generally a pleasurable activity and sitting down to eat your sandwich at lunch time can be a rapid relaxation technique in itself.

Eating healthily can help you to cope better with stress. The physiological effects of stress cause a depletion of our body's resources. Eating healthily can help to maintain the essential balance of vitamins and minerals that we need to combat stress. Also, 'fast' foods tend to be unhealthy foods. They are generally high in fat, salt and sugar. The release of corticosteroids as a chronic response to stress results in elevated blood-cortisol levels which can predispose you to clogging of the arteries. A diet which is high in fat can interact with this with unhealthy consequences for the heart.

A few simple hints can help to reduce the fat and salt in our diets:

- Switch to low-fat versions of foods where possible
- Grill foods instead of frying them
- When you need to use fat in cooking, use cooking oils, rather than solid fats: oils are higher in unsaturated fats and are therefore less likely to block the arteries
- Use a low-fat spread, rather than butter or margarine
- Avoid adding salt when you cook
- Avoid adding salt at the table

Reducing caffeine intake

Caffeine has an effect on blood pressure. It can raise resting systolic pressures by 5 points. This effect lasts for about an hour after we have drunk a strong cup of coffee. This effect appears to be maintained even after many years of caffeine intake—we don't develop tolerance to this effect. If you drink a lot of strong coffee (more than five cups of coffee per day) then you should consider cutting down on your intake. Don't try to stop all at once, as suddenly dropping your caffeine levels to zero can produce withdrawal symptoms such as tiredness, irritability and insomnia. Instead cut down gently. For a week, replace one cup of coffee with a drink that doesn't contain caffeine, such as water, fruit juice, or caffeine-free coffee. The next week replace another cup of coffee. Within a few weeks you will have reduced your level of caffeine intake significantly and without experiencing withdrawal symptoms.

Taking exercise

Taking exercise helps us to cope with stress in two ways. First, people who are aerobically fit are generally better able to cope with stress. Second, physical exercise can be relaxing and helps to ease the stresses and strains of work.

We often think that exercise should be hard work and arduous. It need not be so. In order to increase our aerobic capacity we need to take some form of exercise two or three times a week for about 20 to 30 minutes. The exercise need not be very hard: you should exercise enough to make you feel out of breath, but not so much that you would have difficulty speaking to someone as you exercise.

You can incorporate exercise into your daily routine by making small modifications to how you work. For example, try walking instead of taking the car for short journeys, or climb the stairs instead of taking the lift.

If you feel you would benefit from a more structured approach, think about joining a local gym or sports centre. If you haven't taken any exercise for a long time, before you start any programme of exercise see your general medical practitioner for a check-up. Mention that you are going to take up exercise, and he or she may be able to offer you advice.

Hobbies as stress management

Hobbies provide us with a useful way to take time away from work and to relax. We also receive social support from meeting people when our hobby involves playing a team sport or other team activity. In our interviews with general dental practitioners we found that many dentists identify hobbies as a way of relaxing from the pressures of work. Often these hobbies involved working with your hands—this is not surprising given the manual dexterity required to work in dentistry. Here are a few quotes from the interviews that we carried out:

I play golf.

I dig my garden and after a while the tension just slips away.

I do a lot of work with my hands. Wood work. I have a workshop in my garden and I go there.

These dentists found that hobbies helped to provide relaxation and a distraction from the pressures of work. Try allocating some time to a new hobby, or a hobby that you have neglected through work.

Identifying social support

Having a close friend or confidante to whom we can talk about our worries and stress is a very good protection against the effects of stress. Many research studies have demonstrated that those people who have good social support networks are less likely to experience the harmful effects of stress on their physical and psychological health. We can identify two sources of support:

- Friends and family
- Professional support networks

Sharing our experiences and frustrations with family and friends can be useful in providing an airing ground. Simply talking about difficulties can in itself be comforting. However, sometimes it is useful to be able to talk to someone who is able to offer practical solutions or who may have experienced similar difficulties and understands the intricate details of the problem. In these circumstances it may be useful to talk with other dentists. Your local dental association is a good way of meeting colleagues, which provides support and practical advice.

In general we can identify two types of support that we gain from those around us: *emotional* support and *practical* support. *Emotional* support refers to the boost in our self-esteem and feelings of worth which is given to us by our closest friends and family. Often this is unrelated to the demands we face, and is a general feeling of worth which we gain from those closest to us. *Practical* support, as its name implies, refers to the financial and material support which can be gained from others. At times of great difficulty this can be very important.

Summary

In this chapter we have examined some of the techniques for alleviating stress through lifestyle change. We identified five areas for change:

Learn to relax	Try using the relaxation techniques we have outlined. You should aim to spend half an hour relaxing, once or twice a week.
Change your diet	Cut down on fatty foods. Eat regularly. Aim to sit down to eat three times a day. Cut down on caffeine. Aim for one or two cups of coffee each day. Watch your alcohol intake. Remember, the recommended limit for men is 3 or 4 units daily, for women 2 or 3 units daily.
Take exercise	Aim for twenty to thirty minutes of exercise, two or three times a week.
Hobbies	Consider a hobby as a way of relaxing.
Social support	Identify your sources of support, both personal and professional. Meet your colleagues regularly.

Further reading

Both deal with the lifestyle changes associated with reducing our personal stress levels.

Cooper, C.L., Cooper, R.D. and Eaker, L.H. (1988) *Living with Stress.* London: Penguin.

Freeman, R, Main, J.R.R. and Burke, F.J.T. 'Occupational stress and dentistry: Theory and practice. Part II Assessment and control.' *British Dental Journal*, **178**: 218–22 (1995).

6

Environmental management

The dental environment contains a number of sources of physical stress. There are two key aspects to dealing with these sources of stress, which are: removing the sources of stress by ensuring that the environment is as free of environmental stressors as possible; and alleviating the stress caused by the environment, through exercise and regular breaks. The British Dental Association produces helpful advice sheets and information leaflets about the design of surgeries. You can find the address of the BDA in the back of this book.

We can identify three main sources of environmental stress as follows:

1 Stress and strain on the eyes
2 Stress and strain on the ears
3 Stress and strain on the back and skeleton

Let us examine each of these in turn.

Stress and strain on the eyes

Working in the mouth requires a great deal of concentration and attention to detail. This concentration upon fine work and close detail may create problems of strain on the eyes. Focusing upon an object which is close to us is, in itself, tiring for the eyes. It is important that we take both short- and long-term steps to minimise the possibility of damage to the eyes (see Figure 6.1).

Remember, you only get one pair of eyes and they are an essential part of your job. It is very important to look after them.

Stress and strain on the ears

Another potential source of stress in the dental surgery is noise. The sound of handpieces is particularly stressful since it is of a very high

- Ensure that levels of lighting in the surgery are good. It is important that the lights are sufficient to ensure good levels of light in the operating area.

- Wear protective eye wear. Debris entering the eye may cause immediate or cumulative trauma. This can be minimised by using protective eye wear.

- Take an 'eye rest' at regular intervals. Since focusing on objects at close range is tiring over long periods of time, take a break every half an hour or so by shifting your focus for a few seconds to an object at a greater distance, for example looking out of the window. It does not need to be for very long—about ten seconds is long enough.

- Have your eyes checked regularly. Your eyesight should be checked at least once a year, more often if you have difficulties or problems with your eyes.

Fig. 6.1   Steps to reduce strain on the eyes

frequency and changes often in level and frequency. Exposure to long periods of high frequency noise, even at relatively low levels, can result in hearing loss. In order to avoid these adverse effects, it is important to take regular breaks from the noise, and to have your hearing checked regularly.

Stress and strain on the back and skeleton

One of the greatest sources of physical stress in dentistry is the seating position adopted by the dentist and nurse when working on a patient. Back injuries are common in dentistry and one of the most commonly cited reasons for early retirement. The seating position is an awkward one, and this may be exacerbated by attempts to twist around the patient in order to get direct vision when working in areas which are difficult to see. Often the attempt to get direct vision is a result of time pressures—it is so much easier and quicker to work with direct vision. In an environment where time spent and money earned are directly related, it is tempting to work in the quickest way possible. This may in the long term be counter-productive if working becomes more and more difficult.

You can obtain a very helpful and practical advice sheet on occupational back problems from the British Dental Association (see address at the back of this book). The steps listed in Figure 6.2 are designed to ensure that you place the least possible strain upon the skeleton.

Remember that back injuries are very common among dental practitioners, and take steps to avoid them.

- Ensure that your dental chair and seats are ergonomically correct and at the right height for you and your colleagues.

- Ensure that all the equipment that you routinely use is within easy reach. Often it is tempting to reach across to something that is just out of reach, placing extra strain on your neck and spine.

- Take regular breaks in which you stretch your muscles. Take a break every half hour, stand up and stretch. This should only take a short time but will yield great benefits. Try the exercises given in Figure 6.3.

- Avoid adopting uncomfortable sitting positions which give direct vision. It is better to take a little more time, with less strain on the spine, than to achieve a very quick procedure at the risk of personal injury.

- Take regular exercise. The muscles built up by regular exercise will help to support your skeleton and minimise the strain experienced by your routine work.

- If you experience pains in your back, consult a general medical practitioner. Consider physiotherapy, in particular a practitioner of the Alexander technique. Addresses for such practitioners can be found in the useful addresses section at the back of this book.

Fig. 6.2   Steps to reduce strain on the skeleton

---

1. Neck stretches
Stand or sit upright with your shoulders back. Tilt your head to the left and feel the stretch in the muscles of your neck. Hold for a count of three and return your head to the vertical position. Now tilt your head to the right and again hold for a count of three. Repeat on both sides.

2. Back stretching
Standing upright, join your hands together by intertwining your fingers. Reach both hands directly above your head with your palms pointing upwards and reach as far as you can. Hold for a count of five.

3. Calf stretches
Sitting down, place your feet flat on the floor. Raise your legs by lifting your ankles off the ground and rolling your weight on to your toes. Hold for a count of three and let your feet drop. Repeat.

Fig. 6.3   Stretching exercises for tired muscles

Summary

The dental surgery can place physical stress upon our bodies. The most noticeable sources of physical stress are:

- Strain on the eyes
- Strain on the ears through the noise of the drill
- Strain on the skeleton, in particular the spine, through incorrect sitting position

Minimising these physical stressors depends on two things. First, we must ensure that the environment is as free as possible of physical stressors. This can be achieved by, for example, ensuring that there is good lighting, that chairs are comfortable and supporting and so on. Second, we may need to change our behaviour to ensure that the physical effects of stress are minimised, for example by taking regular breaks, and changing position.

Further reading

The following authors identified that the most common reasons for premature retirement among dentists were musculo-skeletal disorders and stress related symptoms.

Freeman, R., Main, J.R.R. and Burke, F.J.T. 'Occupational stress and dentistry: Theory and practice. Part I Recognition.' *British Dental Journal*, **178**: 214–7 (1995).

Freeman, R., Main, J.R.R. and Burke, F.J.T. 'Occupational stress and dentistry: Theory and practice. Part II Assessment and control.' *British Dental Journal*, **178**: 218–22 (1995).

Burke, F.J., Main, J.R. and Freeman, R. 'The practice of dentistry: An assessment of reasons for premature retirement.' *British Dental Journal*, **182**: 250–4 (1997).

The British Dental Association produces a number of advice sheets and information leaflets which describe the problem of occupational back problems and how these can best be avoided. Additionally the BDA are always willing to provide information about the design of dental surgeries, in order to minimise occupational stress. The address of the BDA can be found in the Appendix.

7

'Stop the world I want to get off': Time management

Time and scheduling pressures have been identified as major stressors in dental practice (Cooper *et al.*, 1987) and we are accustomed to think that there is little that we can do about them. In this chapter we will address the issue of managing time effectively so that we can achieve the goals we have set ourselves. This chapter is organised into three parts as follows:

- Setting our time priorities. Do we work to live or live to work?
- Becoming aware of time. Does time control us or do we control our time?
- Managing time constraints, both those we impose on ourselves and those others impose on us.

Setting our time priorities

It is important to take some time to examine our priorities for using our time. This can be surprising, as it is not often we take the time to ask ourselves these questions. What do we want from our life? Do we work to live or live to work? What are our expectations of work? What are our expectations of leisure? How do we balance the demands of home and work? One way to start thinking about these questions is to look at how you spend your week and compare it with how you would ideally like to spend your time. Draw a circle to represent your week. Now divide the circle up according to how you would ideally like to spend your time.

Now repeat this process, but this time divide the circle up according to how you actually spend your time. It is a good idea to ask a close friend or relative to look at your circle and see if they agree with your perception of how you spend your time. We have given an example in Figure 7.1.

Comparing your two circles, where are the discrepancies? Where are you giving too much time to something, and where are you not giving enough

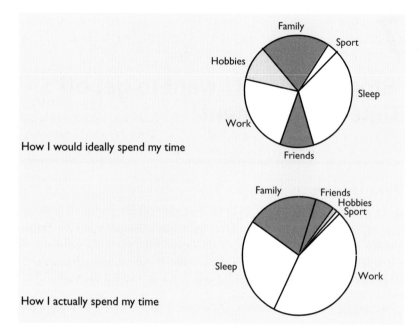

Fig. 7.1   Example of ideal and actual time use diagrams

time to something? In the example given we would like to be spending more time on almost everything, except work, to which we would like to be allocating less time. Note that we wouldn't want to do no work—work can be rewarding and provide satisfaction in its own right, as well as an income.

Having noted the discrepancies, next try to identify why those discrepancies exist. Often we find that this is because there is an implicit set of priorities in operation which identify the lifestyle we would like to have. We may be spending longer hours at the surgery, seeing more patients, in order to increase our income to afford the bigger car, better house, or better school, which we believe is what we and those closest to us want. General dental practitioners are fortunate to have the ability to determine, to a large extent, their income. For the majority of the population, the income or salary is determined for the job role, and the lifestyle coat has to be cut according to that available cloth. In dental practice we are able to vary our hours and income, within reason, to accommodate our needs. This is very advantageous, but can become debilitating if it leads to excessive striving.

It is important in thinking about priorities to consider not only the importance of work, but also other priorities such as health (physical and psychological), relationships and family life.

Look back at your ideal distribution of time. Take this and consider it in conjunction with those closest to you as a basis for setting your priorities for use of your time. It is important that you recognise that in achieving your ideal use of time you will have to make some compromises. These may include sacrificing some material wealth. It is important that you and those closest to you feel comfortable with those compromises.

Becoming aware of time

We all have the same 168 hours per week at our disposal. No one has more time or less time. Perhaps infuriatingly, it cannot be stored and used later in a busy period, nor can it be replaced, for once it's past it's gone forever. We spend it with everything we do. There are no free samples. It has been estimated that each minute of our time costs about 1p for each £1,000 of annual salary. It is vitally important, therefore, how we use our time. On occasions we find 'time flies', on others 'time drags', and yet it is the same time to which we're referring. Clearly the difference between the two time periods is reflected in our attitude to it and what we were doing at the time. This illustrates how bad our memories can be at identifying precisely how we spend our time. The purpose of good time management is to ensure that time, along with all our other available resources, is used to best effect so that we achieve our objectives, be they work or leisure. It is not to try to fill every unforgiving minute with 60 seconds of unremitting activity. Time is a resource which requires good management to enable us to deliver our desired quality of life.

It has been estimated that between 20% and 60% of our time is under our own control. Other people, therefore, control between 40% and 80%. This is true for all of us, and yet some people seem always to be in control of their time whilst others appear never to be so. 'If you want something done, ask a busy person' is only true because 'busy' people use their time effectively and wisely, that is they are organised, have determined their priorities and know when to say no. Such individuals do not appear to be fiercely competitive, rather they are good team players, know what they want from life and have many outside interests. They listen well and when they give their time to you they never appear rushed or under pressure; they have a measured approach to life and take one thing at a time. To them, it appears, personal satisfaction is more important than what others might think, and they tend to be people not afraid of showing their feelings.

Warren and Toll (1993) termed such types *Strollers* and contrasted them with *Dashers*. They developed a useful checklist for looking at these two extremes, which they adapted from Rosenman and Friedman's work (1975) (see Figure 7.2).

DASHER	STROLLER
Never late	Casual about time
Very competitive	Not competitive
Anticipates what others are going to say and finishes it for them	Listens well
Always feels rushed	Never feels rushed even under pressure
Impatient about waiting	Never impatient about waiting
Tries to do too many things at once	Takes things one at a time
Speaks emphatically and fast	Speaks slowly and deliberately
Wants public recognition at work	Personal satisfaction more important than what others think
Walks and eats fast	Does things slowly
Drives self and others hard	Easy-going
Hides feelings	Shows feelings
Few outside interests	Many outside interests
Ambitious	Not ambitious
Eager to get things done	Casual

Fig. 7.2   Checklist to identify Dashers and Strollers

In reviewing this checklist someone probably immediately comes to mind as a typical Dasher or Stroller. Equally it is not difficult to identify which of these two types is going to be more susceptible to a heart attack and which more likely to have achieved a quality of life balance between work and home. Where do you fit between these two extremes? It is possible that you are a different 'type' in different situations. Certainly most of us will be more like a Stroller in our home life, and more of a Dasher at work. This is not unusual. Different situations call for different behaviours. Think about the characteristics of situations which make you more like a Dasher. Mostly these are when we put ourselves under time pressure to achieve large volumes of work in a short space of time. Alternatively it may be that we become more like a Dasher when there is another Dasher about. The Dashing style can be infectious. In contrast, the Stroller style can be infuriating if it interferes with our perceived need to rush. Both styles may in their own way be capable of causing stress in others if the other team members are from the opposite end of the scale. Whilst they may be apparently containing their own stress levels, they may be affecting others, as identified in the saying 'I'm not suffering from stress—but I am a carrier'.

Having decided whether you are mostly Dasher or mostly Stroller, and acknowledging that the Stroller style exhibits more of the characteristics associated with less stress and better time management, it is useful to think about one or two areas where you feel it would be helpful to change your style. Don't try anything dramatic like overnight conversion. This will rarely happen. Rather identify those behaviours you would like to change. Set yourself a target for each change, and then break down your overall target into smaller steps. Then, step by step, work towards your goal. This should not only bring its own reward of achievement, but also enable you to feel more relaxed.

Managing time constraints

If we want to use our time most effectively we need to address two aspects: how to plan the most effective use of our time; and how to manage external demands that take up our time. We will address each of these in turn. In brief the skills required are as below.

How to plan the most effective use of our time:

- Know your goals
- Prioritise your goals
- Allocate time to goals

How to manage external demands that take up our time:

- Define your practice philosophy
- Delegate

How to plan the most effective use of our time

It is important to plan your use of time, after all—if you fail to plan, you plan to fail.

The first step in managing your time is to identify your goals. These may be short term, medium term, or long term, and ideally all three. They should also be achievable. The main purpose behind setting goals is to give a focus on priorities and as a result identify what is most important to be spending time on and to plan and organise accordingly. Earlier we discussed the amount of time we want to spend on various aspects of our lives: friends, work, family and so on. These are our long-term goals, what we want from life and how we would like to spend our time overall. Looking at these goals, there are implications for medium- and short-term goals. Long-term goals will include thinking about where you want to live, family responsibilities, holidays and so on. These have implications for how time is allocated at all levels; when to go on holiday, when in the week to spend time on hobbies, how we book patients, how we organise the practice and so on. The three levels of goals should build upon each other.

The next step in planning your time is to prioritise your goals. This process of prioritising is very important and it requires great self-discipline. Often, when we come to tackle our short-term goals , usually in the form of a 'TO DO' list, we start with the things which seem easier, more interesting, satisfying or urgent. We leave the important issues which we don't like doing, or the unfamiliar jobs we aren't sure how to start, or the easy but uninteresting jobs, to roll over from day to day. Prioritising goals requires placing them in order of importance.

The final step in planning our time use is to allocate time to our goals. Ideally, time should be allocated in proportion to the priority of the goal. This is often difficult in practical terms, because we get distracted by a more interesting (or easier) job which we would prefer to be working on. The Pareto principle suggests that we spend 20% of our time on those tasks which yield 80% of the results and 80% on the relatively unimportant issues which give only 20% of the results. Bearing this in mind, it's worthwhile concentrating time on the areas which will yield the most results with minimum stress. This you need to determine for yourself in association with those closest to you. Write a plan of work and then stick to it as closely as possible—plan your work, and work your plan.

Other difficulties in allocating time arise because our time is 'stolen' by external demands. In the next section we talk about techniques to handle these *time stealers*.

How to manage external demands that take up our time

When we have talked with general dental practitioners about stress, we have met many practitioners who have said that they are ruled by their appointment books. In fact they suggest that this happens to such an extent that they feel unable to take holidays because the diary is fully booked up, and that in order to have a break they would have to cancel patients. This would make them feel guilty and would also create resentment and hassle amongst both patients and staff. The problem here is that work is controlling you rather than you controlling work. In this instance your time is not your own, it is stolen by demands from others (patients and staff). To deal with this we need to identify a practice philosophy, and to develop skills of delegation.

A practice philosophy will cover the following areas:

- The aims and objectives of the practice
- How everyone associated with the practice can be expected to be treated
- Appointment systems
- Protocols for dealing with emergency requests, telephone interruptions, drop-in visitors
- Duties and responsibilities of all colleagues

In designing a practice philosophy it is important that all colleagues agree on the philosophy, that all understand their duties and responsibilities as a result of the philosophy, and that the philosophy is regularly reviewed to determine whether it is still relevant.

There are many aspects of the day-to-day running of a practice which should be identified as potential time stealers. Some of these are listed in Figure 7.3. A practice protocol should outline how these will be handled.

The development of a practice philosophy will tell us a lot about ourselves. Do I trust others in the practice? Am I frightened of missing out on something if not all decisions are referred to me? Do I like to feel indispensable? Do I delegate? Do I delegate but then interfere? Do I delegate and then abdicate responsibility? Am I expecting staff colleagues to be clones of myself? Do I delegate a series of tasks to be performed or do I delegate a result to be achieved? There are many routes to the same endpoint, and different people may use different routes.

Having decided on your practice philosophy, you may have identified a need to delegate some tasks. Delegation requires good communication and the acceptance of risk. It also values and trusts colleagues. Many of the duties within a busy practice can be delegated—the critical question to ask ourselves is, 'Must I do this myself or is there some other way of achieving the same end?' Do not delegate only the tedious tasks, otherwise this will be disheartening for colleagues.

I. **Interruptions**
   (a) Casual callers/visitors.
       Should they be seen straight away, later or not at all?
       Could they be seen by someone else?
   (b) Telephone calls.
       In what circumstances should/could you be interrupted—if any?
       Could a message be taken and/or phone back?
   (c) Patients.
       What is the priority of a patient in the reception area over a
       telephone caller?
       What is the priority of a patient in the reception area over other
       staff, including yourself?

2. **Information**
   Have you identified what information you need, for patients, for ordering,
   for budgeting?
   Is the information you receive timely and accurate?
   How much detail do you need?

3. **Paperwork**
   Does it require your attention? Any piece of paper should be read and
   dealt with once—take action at the time.
   Keep reports short and simple. Remember the 3-minute rule—people
   will usually read straight away something which can be dealt with within
   3 minutes (about 600 words).
   Share journals with colleagues—mark important and interesting points
   with a highlighter and concentrate only on that which is relevant to you.
   Always carry reading material with you just in case you have to wait.

4. **Meetings**
   If you have to attend meetings clarify for yourself the following issues:
   Why is the meeting being held?
   What does the meeting hope to accomplish?
   Does the meeting have a stated purpose, start time and finish time?
   Have you prepared for the meeting?
   Are you going to speak to any items?
   Is it a good use of time?

5. **Telephone calls**
   Do you prepare for phone calls before you make them—is all the
   relevant information to hand?
   Have you got something you can do whilst listening to the 'canned' music
   if you are having to hold on?
   If you are unable to make contact with the appropriate person, have you
   agreed a time to call back, and have you kept the phone number to hand?
   Do you have a polite but firm way of ending an overlong call?

Fig. 7.3   Ways of reducing 'time stealers'

Some people may experience difficulty in delegating. Certainly, those of us who are Dashers, as identified earlier, are likely to be poor at delegation whilst Strollers will probably feel more comfortable in this role. If you find it difficult to delegate, try starting with something small. When this is successful it may build your confidence to delegate bigger tasks.

Summary

In managing your time, there are three broad steps.

1. Identify your priorities and goals.

The first step in managing your time is identifying how you want to spend your time, and what you want from each aspect of your life. These two aspects may conflict. Decide, in conjunction with those closest to you, how you want to spend your time.

2. Examine your habitual style of dealing with time.

Are you a Dasher or a Stroller? If you are a Dasher, could you benefit from a little more strolling?

3. Manage your own time, and external demands on your time.

Plan your use of time by:

- Identifying long-term, medium-term and short-term goals (remember goals should be achievable)
- Prioritising your goals
- Allocating time, on a day-to-day basis, to achieving your goals

Build a practice philosophy (see Figure 7.4 overleaf) which includes protocols for dealing with external demands on your time (*time stealers*). Delegate duties (give yourself more time by using other people's time).

Does the practice philosophy contain the following?
- The aims and objectives of the practice
- How everyone associated with the practice can be expected to be treated
- Appointment systems
- Protocols for dealing with emergency requests, telephone interruptions, drop-in visitors
- Duties and responsibilities of all colleagues

Are all colleagues aware of the practice philosophy?

Do all colleagues agree to work to the practice philosophy?

Fig. 7.4   Checklist of your practice philosophy

Further reading

Useful guides to principles and techniques of time management.

Tysoe, M. (1988) *All this and work too*. London: Fontana.

Austin, B. (1986) 'Making effective use of executive time.' London: *Management Update*.

Seymour-Smith, L. (1984) 'Making your meetings more effective.' London: *Management Update*.

8

Personnel management

In this chapter we will discuss managing personnel to achieve the best results and to minimise stress. This chapter will build upon the previous chapter, where we identified the principles of developing a practice philosophy and achieving goals through delegation. If we are to delegate effectively we need to have the right people working with us, and to manage them effectively.

The art of personnel management involves the following steps:

- Identifying the right people for your team
- Communicating with your team
- Effective team working
- Addressing problems within the team
- Handling change within the work environment

We will examine each of these aspects of personnel management in turn.

Identifying the right people for your team

Making the right appointment is likely to improve working relationships, reduce strains and increase the effectiveness of the working group. The investment we make in team members can be expensive if it goes wrong.

The first step in choosing your team is to know yourself. By knowing your own strengths and weaknesses it is possible to identify the type of team you need to complement and strengthen your own personality. Take some time to answer the questions in Figure 8.1.

The answers to these questions will help to identify the type of team that you currently have, their goals and ways of working. This will help you to identify the most effective way of managing your team.

Communicating with your team

Good communication takes time, and often when we are stressed we feel we don't have that time. Yet effective communication within the team is

- What are my personal strengths? It might be that you are quick and efficient at work, that you are friendly and relaxed with your staff.

- What are my personal weaknesses? Do you always communicate what you want? Do you sometimes get annoyed when things don't go exactly your way?

- What are the short and long term goals of my practice team?

- What motivates my team members and colleagues to work? Why do they work with me?

- What are my team members and colleagues seeking from work?

- What has worked well for me and the team in the past? What has not worked well?

Fig. 8.1   Identifying your strengths and weaknesses

very important. The key to good communication is to take time to be relaxed and approachable, to be observant and above all to listen. A good maxim to work by is the suggestion that a good manager should earn 90% of their salary by listening to others, and should spend 60% of their time in face-to-face contact with other people. Listening has both verbal and non-verbal components. The non-verbal components include looking at the person, nodding and saying 'Mmm' at appropriate points. Verbal components include asking open questions in order to develop under-standing, checking and paraphrasing what has been said, reflecting it back to the speaker. Through this process of listening to your team, you will get to know them and be in a position to answer some of the questions that we posed at the start of the chapter.

Effective team working

When teams form, and also when new members enter a team, it is quite usual for the group to go through the processes shown in Figure 8.2.

Once a team is formed and working well, there is an interdependency of members. It is useful to draw up a dependency diagram (see Figure 8.3) in order to examine the inter-relationships of team members. Place yourself in the centre and then identify in each balloon the other people you rely on to do your job.

Now either extend the diagram or draw a new one to identify those who rely on you. It also identifies quite clearly that the introduction of new team

- Forming   Members settle down, each being polite to the other.
- Storming   Differences arise, arguments happen, there are tensions associated with the development of the group's goals.
- Norming   Strengths and weaknesses of each of the members are recognised, patterns of behaviour in the group are established. The team gels and recognises the need to pull together.
- Performing   All the team members pull together and in the same direction.
- Mourning   When the team breaks up, or results are achieved.

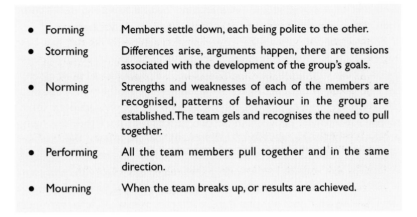

Fig. 8.2   The processes involved in forming a team

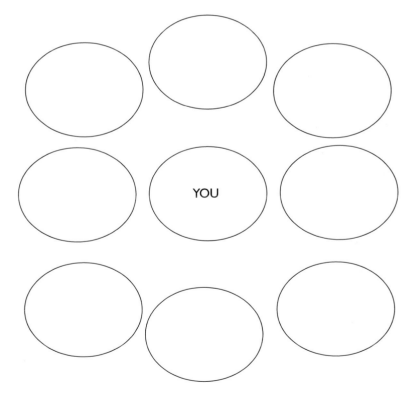

Fig. 8.3   Dependency diagram

members or the loss of old ones requires careful handling, good communication and the involvement of important team members.

Show appreciation for what your team has achieved. Teams grow best and develop most when they are given positive feedback and encouragement. Those who grow least are those who hear nothing and must assume they are doing all right because no one has told them otherwise. Curiously those who receive negative feedback or who are reprimanded are intermediate in growth between these two groups—at least they are being noticed! Whilst most people go out to work to earn money, they also out to do a good job. If they achieve this, then it should be acknowledged. A 'Thank You' culture in the team is difficult to introduce. It is almost as if we feel that if someone has been praised today, it will be harder to discipline them if they do something wrong tomorrow. All team members should be able to give and receive a 'Thank You' reward from each other, even the team leader. Equally all team members should be advised of how they are doing against their agreed objectives. These objectives should relate to the overall objectives of the practice. Each member of the team should be able to identify their contribution to the success of the practice, and be rewarded accordingly. The skill of the team leader lies in identifying the abilities of their team and setting them objectives on the basis of those talents. Open communication through team meetings and day-to-day discussions will increase the likelihood that your team are committed to the objectives of the practice.

Participation + Involvement = Commitment + Ownership

Addressing problems within the team

Ideally it is best to deal with issues as they occur. If problems or conflicts build up they can cause unnecessary tensions. This may be difficult in the surgery situation with patients continually coming and going. In this situation it may only be necessary to say to your colleague that you are aware that there is an issue which needs addressing. It is very useful to have team meetings at which issues can be aired and discussed. A fixed day and time for such meetings is useful, for example every Monday morning for the first half hour of the day. Encourage all the team members to bring items for discussion and give them equal value. Discuss what went well in the previous week, what didn't go quite so well and how it might be better in the future. Be open and not defensive in your responses.

When team members are not performing well, the issue needs to be addressed. Don't be a Friday manager. The Friday manager leaves all the bad news until the end of the week—and probably the end of Friday—before imparting it. This probably happens because, understandably, we are unhappy at having to address the problem with the team member and, after Friday, there's a weekend to not have to face them and live with the immediate consequences. Often, however, the weekend becomes a time for brooding and so by Monday matters are worse and not better. If an issue is important enough to address, it is better to do so when there is enough of the working week left, so that the people involved may be supported through the process of improvement. Any feedback that you give to a person should be aimed at what they have or have not done, and not to their personality. Feedback should be given helpfully and constructively, giving examples to show not only how it was but also how you would like it to be. Such occasions are stressful for everyone concerned. It is helpful to consider the risks and rewards of action. It is all too easy to overestimate the risks of such an action and to underestimate the rewards.

Handling change within the work environment

One of the areas of personnel management which is perhaps the most difficult to deal with is change. Change tends to be perceived as a threat to security and perceived control over the situation. As we have seen in Chapter 2, perceived lack of control is stressful. The reactions of colleagues will depend in part upon what they have heard about the proposed changes. In most organisations, informal communication networks work much faster than the formal lines of communication. To implement changes successfully requires a basis of trust. In order to build this trust it is important that team members are appraised of proposed changes early on, whether these changes concern work practices, organisation or staffing, so that they are given an opportunity to comment on them and modify them. The implementation process should take place alongside an appropriate training and education strategy. All too often we assume that members of the team will learn a new skill or adapt to a new situation on their own. This process of change may occur as a result of very small changes in practical issues such as the introduction of a new restorative material—for which the dental nurse is expected to know how to produce the perfect mix just by reading the instruction leaflet—to the introduction of a new team member, who has been chosen without the involvement of the others.

Trust is important in working as a team, especially during periods of change. Trust your team members, unless they prove to be untrustworthy.

Summary

Personnel management is a key aspect of working in teams. In order to manage your personnel well it is important to:

- Know yourself, your management style and career objectives
- Identify the characteristics of your team members, and their inter-relationships
- Communicate effectively with the members of your team
- Deal effectively with problems that arise in the team
- Identify the difficulties that arise when changes occur in the team and work through these

Further reading

A guide to people management, principles and practice.

Drucker, P. (1977) *People and Performance*. London: Heinemann.

Two useful introductions to transactional analysis—a technique for understanding the behaviour of other people, including work colleagues.

Harris, T.A. (1973) *I'm OK—You're OK*. London: Pan.
Berne, E. (1968) *Games People Play*. Harmondsworth: Penguin.

A comprehensive description of the processes of interaction, which covers non-verbal behaviour as well as verbal interactions.

Argyle, M. (1986) *The Psychology of Interpersonal Behaviour*. Harmondsworth: Penguin.

A good introduction to team working team types, their respective qualities and interactions.

Belbin, R.M. (1981) *Management Teams: Why they succeed or fail*. London: Heinemann.

Useful guides to understanding stress and its impact on individuals and teams.

Warren, E. and Todd, C. (1993) *The Stress Workbook*. London: Nicholas Brearley in association with the Industrial Society.
Rozenman, R.H. and Friedmann, M. 'Coronary heart disease: the Western Collaborative Group study'. *Journal of the American Medical Association*, **233**: 872–7 (1975).
Cooper, C.C., Watts, J. and Kelly, M. 'Job satisfaction, mental health and job stressors among general dental practitioners in the UK'. *British Dental Journal*, **24**: 77–88 (1987).

9

Changing behaviour

The effects of stress on behaviour can be divided into three broad categories:

- Stress and health related behaviour
- Stress and the general disruption of behaviour
- Stress and critical incidents

Stress and health related behaviour

When we are stressed, there tends to be a change in several of our behaviours which are related to health or ill health. Look down the checklist given in Figure 9.1 and check how many of the behaviours listed are affected by your stress.

Increase smoking	☐
Eat more	☐
Eat less	☐
Change the type of food you eat	☐
Drink more alcohol	☐
Take less exercise	☐

Fig. 9.1 Behaviour affected by stress

In general the effects of stress are to make our lifestyle less healthy. This interacts with the physiological effects of stress to create an overall negative effect of stress on our health. It is important to recognise these harmful changes and take action to prevent them.

Smoking

Tobacco smoking is extremely harmful to health. Stopping smoking has a profound impact upon your health, decreasing your risk of dying from a whole range of diseases. However, once started, smoking is a very difficult habit to break. If you want to give up smoking, seek the advice of your general medical practitioner. She or he will be able to give you information about local 'quit smoking' groups in your area. When you decide to quit smoking follow these steps:

- Choose a time to stop which is likely to be easier than other times. A particularly stressful time of year is probably not a good idea.
- Pick a day to stop. A good idea is to select a day that you will remember—an anniversary or another significant day.
- Consider using nicotine supplements, and gradually cutting down on the supplements.
- Let everyone know that you are trying to stop, ask for their help and support.

Refer to the list we have given in the Appendix of sources of support for help in giving up smoking.

Drinking

Be aware of the amount of alcohol you drink. Try counting the number of units that you take each week. The recommended safe limits are for men 3 or 4 units daily and for women 2 or 3 units daily. A unit of alcohol is equivalent to one half pint of beer or a pub measure of spirits. Remember that the measures you serve at home are likely to be bigger than those you are given in pubs and restaurants. If you find that your levels are quite high, then you should seriously consider cutting down. There are a few simple things that you can do to help cut down:

- Try alternating soft drinks with alcoholic drinks. This way you can cut your intake by half.
- Avoid buying big rounds of drinks because then you have drinks bought back for you, and end up drinking much more than you had planned.
- Try having a few 'drink-free' days each week.
- Avoid drinking on your own or 'to relax', instead try taking some exercise or the relaxation exercises we listed in Chapter 5.
- Find alternative ways of socialising which don't involve drinking, for example playing bowls, or five-a-side football.

We have provided a list of sources of support if you feel you need more help with cutting down on your drinking. See the Appendix at the end of the book.

Eating

When we are stressed it is all too easy to rush meals and to choose food which is convenient and quick. In Chapter 5 we discussed the importance of eating a healthy diet which contains a broad range of foodstuffs, and to take time to eat our food. Compare what you eat in a typical day in practice with your diet for a typical day when you are not in practice. How does your diet differ? On which day do you eat more healthily? If you find that you want to improve your diet and ensure that you have more time to sit and enjoy your food, you will need to examine your time management (see Chapter 7).

Your general medical practitioner will be able to provide you with detailed information about healthy eating.

Exercise

Allocate time to taking exercise. In order to maintain a good level of aerobic fitness, we need to perform some form of exercise two or three times a week, for a period of 20 to 30 minutes each time. This exercise does not have to be strenuous, just sufficient to make you a little short of breath. Begin by allocating time for exercise in your week. Try to space each of the sessions out—don't do all your week's exercise on three consecutive days and then spend the rest of the week in pain! Next choose a form of exercise that you enjoy, you're more likely to persist in doing something which is fun as well as good for you.

Remember, if you haven't taken any exercise for a long time, consult your general medical practitioner before deciding on a course of strenuous exercise.

Stress and the general disruption of behaviour

As we discussed in Chapter 3, the effects of stress are to reduce our repertoire of behaviours. In general, when we are stressed we tend to behave in a narrow range of ways which are not necessarily as effective as they might be. For example when we are faced with a big stressor such as an overload of patients, what do we do? Do we try to carry on what we are doing, working harder, or for longer, skipping lunch breaks and staying behind in the surgery? Or do we step back from the problem and try to achieve more creative solutions. If the increased demand is short-lived is it possible to employ a locum, or to re-book some patients? Can each patient's course of treatment be split into smaller units so that they need less time, but more appointments over a longer period of time? Is it time to think about expanding the practice?

These general effects of stress on behaviour need to be addressed systematically. We have outlined a technique for analysing the effects of stress on our behaviour and a method for thinking up alternative ways of behaving. This is the Behavioural Analysis of Stress Events (BASE). An example is given in Figure 9.3 opposite.

The first step in this analysis is to think about the nature of the event that sparked the behaviour. What event or events preceded the behaviour? Usually we find that there is a gradual build-up of pressure which suddenly (because of a deadline or because the pressure reaches a critical mass) becomes a problem. In the example we give there is a build-up of paperwork.

Next we identify our current coping strategies. In the example given we cope by trying to stay late, after a hard day's work, to complete the work.

The third step is to identify alternative ways of behaving. The emphasis here is to try to think of a broad range of strategies, without worrying too much about which are practical and which are not. Some broad categories of alternative strategies might be as shown in Figure 9.2.

- **D**elegate. Can you give this work to someone else?

- **D**ivide. Can this task or job be split into smaller components which are more achievable?

- **D**ivert. Is there a different way of tackling the problem?

- **D**iscuss with colleagues the nature of the problems and seek their help and support in solving the problem.

- **D**evelop. Learn new skills to help you deal with the problem. In Chapter 2 we said that stress resulted from a mismatch between demands and ability. One way to tackle stress is to change the demand, but we can also change our ability.

Fig. 9.2   A list of coping strategies

Finally we need to think about the possible barriers that prevent us from implementing these new behavioural strategies. These may take many different forms, but often the barriers we perceive relate to the difficulty of making any change—'People won't like it', 'We've always done it this

What was the event that sparked this behaviour?

Discovered that I had a huge pile of paperwork to go through, in particular our returns to the DPB were late and I was concerned that we wouldn't get paid for this month's work, and have a real cash-flow problem.

What did I do?

Stayed after work to catch up on paperwork from the practice. Spent about an hour working well, then was so tired that I fell asleep in the chair for a bit. Woke up and stayed for another two hours to try to finish work. Felt I wasn't very efficient. Eventually got home at 10.30pm. Ate food and went to bed. Woke up very tired and spent rest of the day shattered. Thought about staying late again but too tired.

What else could I have done?

1. I could have made sure that I was up-to-date with my paperwork all the time.
2. I could employ a practice manager to do all the paperwork.
3. I could allocate an hour a night to the paperwork, and start early enough each month to make sure I get everything done in time each month.
4. I could delegate the work to one of the reception team.

What were the barriers to me doing that?

Barriers in the situation

There just isn't enough time in the week to do the paperwork
The practice isn't computerised, which makes finding the data more difficult
I don't think we can afford to employ someone to do this work

Barriers in my thoughts

I find it difficult to trust the nurses to do the job right
I should really be able to manage this work myself
I should stay at work until I've finished all this work

Other people as barriers

My colleagues won't want to employ a practice manager

Other barriers

I'm too tired to do all this work on top of seeing patients

Fig. 9.3 An example of a BASE analysis

way and it's too difficult to change now'—or difficulties in trusting that the new methods will really work, particularly if they involve giving the responsibility to someone else. In examining these barriers it is important to be honest and ask whether the things you have listed really are barriers or whether they can be overcome with a little effort. In the example given many of the 'barriers' identified are about our perceptions and thoughts—'I should be able to do all this paperwork'. This is not necessarily true particularly if you have a lot of work during the day; it is unreasonable to expect yourself to then put in long hours in the evening to catch up on paperwork. Changing these thoughts and assumptions can be difficult. In the next chapter we talk about how to start doing this.

Stress and critical incidents

In a survey of the stress experienced by dentists (Cooper *et al.* 1988) it emerged that rare but potentially very dangerous events, such as a patient experiencing an anaphylactic shock, were experienced as highly stressful. These events are stressful because they are unpredictable and uncontrollable, and they are potentially very serious. Such *critical incidents* may not be confined to events with patients: we may face extreme stress outside work which has an impact upon our work lives—the death of somebody close, divorce etc.

In dealing with critical incidents we need to take three steps.

1. Recognise the impact of the event upon ourselves

Often we try to deny that an event has had a major impact upon us. We don't like to admit that we are feeling shocked and vulnerable. Also we are usually very reluctant to admit if we are finding it difficult to cope. Sharing these feelings with those closest to you can help to put those feelings in perspective. If you are feeling stressed by an event, it is likely that they will be feeling the same way, and sharing that will give everyone a feeling of being understood.

2. Identify sources of support

It is important to realise that we need support and help to get us through the stress caused by a critical incident. We discuss the importance of social support in coping with stress in Chapter 5. Remember, the immediate fall-out of an event is usually short-lived and people are usually very willing to help in these circumstances. The support we need during times of severe stress falls into two broad categories: practical and emotional. In the immediate aftermath of a major event we usually find it difficult to concentrate, and our usual routines are disrupted. Friends and colleagues can help here by taking on some of the practical responsibilities. It would be nice to have some of our duties eased.

Help with the *feelings* that we have about critical incidents, the emotional side, can come from any of those we are closest to—our partner, family or close friends. Alternatively, it may help to talk about those feelings to someone who is neutral and who is trained to listen and help with emotional problems. This person could be a counsellor, psychologist or psychotherapist. There is no shame in seeing any of these professionals. Your general medical practitioner will be able to help you find a professional in your area. Alternatively, you could contact a group such as the British Association for Counselling in the UK, whose address is given in the Appendix.

3. Review the critical incident, learn from it and put it in its proper place

It is important to take the time to review the critical incident that occurred and examine whether there are any lessons which can be learnt from it. For example, if the incident involved an adverse reaction in a patient, is there any equipment that you feel it would be useful to have in your surgery, or is there any training you or your staff could undertake in order to cope with similar incidents? There may also be other lessons for us to learn about our way of coping with stress or how we interact with other people.

Finally, it is important that after a time we put the critical event in its proper place. Often we find that people dwell on a major event and are worrying that it may happen again. This is illustrated in the following quote, taken from a dentist we interviewed about stress:

> *The worst thing is I had a patient with an anaphylactic shock on me twelve to eighteen months ago which was just the most horrendous thing ever and so now every local I'm doing, I'm waiting for it to happen again and I'm living in fear basically.*

Although they are very stressful when they happen, critical incidents should be relatively rare. Don't let what happened once worry you every day for the rest of your working career. The cognitive restructuring exercises we discuss in Chapter 10 will help you to put the incident in perspective.

Summary

Stress has an impact on behaviour in three broad ways:

1. Unhealthy behaviours

Stress tends to increase our unhealthy behaviours. We should be aware specifically of changes in: smoking, eating, drinking and exercise. If you react to stress by unhealthy behaviours, take some time to change these. Help is available from many sources including voluntary agencies and your general medical practitioner.

2. Coping behaviour

Stress tends to decrease our range of coping behaviours. We have provided a systematic approach to modifying behaviour—the Behavioural Analysis of Stress Events (BASE). A form for doing this is shown in Figure 9.4.

3. Critical incidents

Stress sometimes comes as a critical incident out of the blue. In coping with these events you need to:

- Own up to your stress
- Ask for practical help
- Ask for help with your feelings
- Take time to think about the stress and how to avoid it in the future

Further reading

A good introduction to modifying stress-related behaviour. This book contains much useful advice.

Cooper, C.L., Cooper, R.D. and Eaker, L.H. (1988) *Living with Stress*. London: Penguin.

One of the original books to look at the effects of stress on behaviour and the harmful effects of that behaviour upon health.

Friedman, M. and Rosenman, R.H. (1974) *Type A: Your Behaviour and Your Heart*. New York: Knopf.

A useful publication dealing with the emotional stress of working in health professions.

Bailey, R.D. (1985) *Coping with Stress in Caring*. London: Blackwell Scientific Publications.

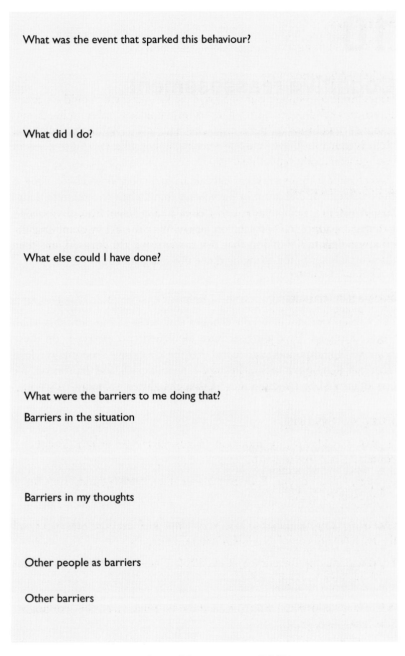

What was the event that sparked this behaviour?

What did I do?

What else could I have done?

What were the barriers to me doing that?
Barriers in the situation

Barriers in my thoughts

Other people as barriers

Other barriers

Fig. 9.4 Behavioural Analysis of Stress Events (BASE)

10

Cognitive reassessment

This chapter is about the way we think. In particular we will be looking at the changes that can occur in the way we think when we are under long-term stress. In general there is a change in thinking from a positive outlook to a negative one, and focusing on failure. We will start by examining the types of negative thinking that occur when we are stressed and then discuss techniques for changing those thought patterns.

Negative thinking

In Chapter 3 we discussed the changes that occur in our thoughts when we are stressed. Psychologists have identified specific types of these negative thoughts, and have found that these negative thoughts can lead to negative emotions such as low self-esteem, anxiety and depression. We can identify 11 broad categories of thoughts, listed in Figure 10.1.

- Perfectionism
- The tyranny of the shoulds
- Black and white thinking
- Overgeneralisation
- Selective focus
- Discounting the positive
- Jumping to conclusions
- Magnification
- Emotional reasoning
- Negative labelling
- Personalising and blaming

Fig. 10.1   Negative thought patterns (after Burns, 1990)

Taking each of these in turn we can define each of the categories and identify examples. As we go through the list, try to think of examples from your own experience. It is important that we understand these categories, because by recognising when we are falling into the trap of thinking about things in a negative way, we can change our thoughts and so feel less stressed.

Perfectionism

'Perfectionism' has been defined in many different ways, but most people agree that it refers to setting very high standards of performance for yourself. In itself this is not a bad thing, but problems arise when the standards that are set become a source of criticism. For example, if we set ourselves a certain standard of excellence for all restorations as a target, it may be that on a given day we fail in this target for 20% of treatments. If we then go home and worry that we are bad dentists because we failed in this target, and believe that we have failed, then we are likely to experience many negative emotions. Alternatively we can use this failure to reach the target as a useful tool for planning: Was the target unrealistic? Did we allocate enough time to do each restoration, given that we want to reach this target? What is a 'good enough' restoration?

This type of 'personal perfectionism' has been identified as a source of stress for many dentists (Godwin *et al.* 1981).

The tyranny of the shoulds

How much of our time do we spend thinking or saying 'I should …'? It doesn't really matter what follows, but it could be one of many things: I should … eat less, take more exercise, spend more time at home, work longer hours, see more patients, earn more money. Sometimes we vary this practice by saying 'I really should …'. The key aspect is the moral imperative of the word 'should'. Try replacing with the phrase 'would like to' instead of 'should'. Immediately it becomes a choice to do whatever follows.

The tyranny of the shoulds refers to the situation where we are hedged in by many, many imperatives, all of which demand our time. Since each is a 'should', it is hard to prioritise between them. By acknowledging that perhaps not all 'shoulds' have the same degree of urgency, we can identify our true priorities and allocate time more effectively in line with our true priorities (see also Chapter 7).

Black and white thinking

As we become more stressed, our thinking becomes more and more polarised, or *black and white*. We label events, beliefs and attitudes in terms such as good versus bad, right or wrong. Very little consideration is given to the middle ground and compromise. For example, we can only think of work as being entirely bad—forgetting the good aspects of our jobs. When we are very stressed our day at work stretches before us bleakly and it is very difficult to think about what is good, except perhaps going home in the evening!

Overgeneralisation

We all have a tendency to overgeneralise, that is to draw conclusions on the basis of a very small amount of evidence. For instance, it is very easy to dwell upon a single mistake, and to blame ourselves. Focusing upon one mistake ignores the many other occasions upon which we have performed the same treatment or task without making a mistake. There is an error of thinking here: we are taking a single instance and imagining that the same thing will always happen.

Other examples may not even be within your control. Previously, in Chapter 9, we discussed a dentist who had experienced a patient having an anaphylactic shock. He had commented:

> *The worst thing is I had a patient with an anaphylactic shock on me twelve to eighteen months ago which was just the most horrendous thing ever and so now every local I'm doing, I'm waiting for it to happen again and I'm living in fear basically.*

Although this is a very distressing thing to happen to any dentist, the person in this quote is clearly overgeneralising. He is focusing on one very distressing occasion and ignoring the thousands of other times he has given a local anaesthetic without the patient suffering this distress.

Selective focus

The examples we have given previously also show elements of selective focus. We tend only to pick out certain facts from any situation and use those facts to explain what happened. In particular we tend to interpret behaviour in terms of enduring personal traits and personality, rather than looking at how the situation determines our behaviour. For example, a colleague who is regularly late for work by five or ten minutes may not be 'lazy' or 'not very good at time-keeping', but may have responsibilities such as dropping off children, or difficulties with transport. They may also be experiencing difficulty sleeping because they (like us) are experiencing symptoms of stress. Patients who are 'unco-operative' or 'difficult' may in fact be behaving as they are because they are nervous, because of the way they have been greeted in the surgery, because they have been kept waiting, or because of a number of other factors.

Related to this, we also tend to focus on what we don't have, the negative aspects of our life, rather than on the positive achievements we have made. This is known as *discounting the positive.*

Jumping to conclusions

We tend to reach conclusions very quickly. Because of the other biases in our thinking the conclusion is usually a negative one. If a colleague is upset or curt with us, we assume that it is our fault. Also we tend to draw conclusions about the future based on the present: a patient who is upset at one appointment becomes a 'difficult patient' who is always upset about something.

Magnification

This is what we call the type of thinking where we give most of our attention to negative events or characteristics. For example, we look down the list for tomorrow's patients and see the name of a patient who was very upset last time we saw him. It is very easy to magnify our worries about that particular patient and let them cloud our entire day.

Emotional reasoning

This refers to the process whereby we draw conclusions on the basis of how we are feeling, rather than on what actually happened. When we are feeling stressed, it is very easy to reason that it is all the fault of the 'inefficient' staff or the 'useless' equipment. We are drawing conclusions on the basis of our feelings, rather than looking at what is actually causing those feelings.

Negative labelling

This refers to the practice of labelling a person because of their behaviour. Everyone makes mistakes and everyone sometimes does work which is not as good as they would like. Just because we do these things does not mean that we are a bad dentist or a bad person.

Personalisation and blaming

Personalisation is the term we give to the process where people accept responsibility for something that has occurred but over which they had no control. A patient who was in a bad mood before they got to the surgery is not in a bad mood because of you personally. Blaming is a similar process, but instead of blaming ourselves, we blame the other person. Neither way of thinking is likely to be entirely accurate.

How can we change these thoughts?

Changing the way we think about things is very difficult. We tend not to question our thoughts and so get very little practice at examining whether our conclusions are reasonable. Also many of the thoughts we have talked about above are *automatic*—they occur very quickly and seem very natural. It is only by developing a critical eye for automatic thoughts that we can start to change them. In order to do this we would like to introduce a formal technique. It is useful to start with this technique as a method of beginning to analyse thoughts. After a while we hope to be able to do away with the formal technique and come to analyse our thoughts almost as automatically as the thoughts themselves occur!

Critical analysis of thoughts

Although our thoughts occur all the time, it is useful to start by examining critical situations. Think over your last week at work. When did you feel most stressed? Taking the form in Figure 10.3, entitled 'Critical Analysis of Stress Events' (CASE), note down that event in the box marked 'Event'. Now write down in the next box how you felt in that situation, including physiological symptoms and emotions. Perhaps you felt angry, annoyed, your palms were sweaty and your heart was beating fast. In the third box we want you to note all the thoughts that you had about that situation, at the time and subsequently. You will probably find this difficult at first. We have provided an example in Figure 10.2, which might help you to see what kind of thoughts we mean.

So far we have listed what happened to you. The next two steps are about trying to change those thoughts. First, using the list provided, categorise your thoughts into the 11 groups we outlined. You may find that you want to use several categories and that you find it difficult to separate out some of the categories. This is not a problem; there is a great overlap between the categories. Second, having decided on the negative nature of your thoughts, rephrase your thoughts into more positive versions. In using this technique we have found that people find this the most difficult part and it takes some practice. (Take some time to examine the example we have given.) Often it is interesting to take the more 'positive' versions and analyse them for the negative thought patterns analysed. In the example given we might have said 'I should give Mr Smith more time'. That would

What happened?

Mr Smith complained about his denture. This is the fourth time he has been back with it and still isn't happy–he says that he would prefer his old set back, despite the fact that they were loose and were causing him mouth ulcers. He says that his previous dentist was much better.

What did I feel?

Felt myself getting very hot under the collar. Got a bit short with Mr Smith, didn't want to listen to him going on and on any more. Felt like telling him to take his old dentures if he thought they were so brilliant. Worried about the amount of time this was taking and the queue that was building up outside.

What did I think?

No matter what I do he will never be happy

My dentures are rubbish

Mr Smith is a difficult patient

Mr Smith thinks I'm a bad dentist

I should be able to make him a set of dentures that he will be happy with

I haven't got time for this

What types of thoughts are those? (tick all those that apply)

- Perfectionism ✓
- The tyranny of shoulds ✓
- Black and white thinking ✓
- Overgeneralisation ✓
- Selective focus ✓
- Discounting the positive ✓
- Jumping to conclusions ✓
- Magnification
- Emotional reasoning
- Negative labelling ✓
- Personalising and blaming ✓

What could I have thought?

My dentures are well made. They function well and look good. I have many patients who have expressed satisfaction with their dentures. Mr Smith has experienced some difficulties adjusting to the new dentures. I need to think about allocating him an extra long appointment to ensure that his concerns are addressed. This may be more efficient than lots of little appointments that don't satisfy either him or me. Ultimately though it may be that Mr Smith would prefer another dentist–this is not a bad reflection on me, I can't get on with everyone!!!

Fig. 10.2   An example of a CASE assessment

What happened?

What did I feel?

What did I think?

What types of thoughts are those?
(tick all those that apply)

- Perfectionism
- The tyranny of shoulds
- Black and white thinking
- Overgeneralisation
- Selective focus
- Discounting the positive
- Jumping to conclusions
- Magnification
- Emotional reasoning
- Negative labelling
- Personalising and blaming

What could I have thought?

Fig. 10.3   Critical Analysis of Stress Events (CASE)

have been a 'should', whereas it is better to give yourself the option of thinking about it.

This critical analysis technique can be used in the formal way described. But we would hope that eventually you will be able to identify when you are thinking negatively even as it happens, and reframe your thoughts into more positive terms.

Summary

When we become stressed, we think negatively about ourselves and our situations. The types of negative thoughts we have can be sorted into 11 groups:

1 Perfectionism
2 The tyranny of the shoulds
3 Black and white thinking
4 Overgeneralisation
5 Selective focus
6 Discounting the positive
7 Jumping to conclusions
8 Magnification
9 Emotional reasoning
10 Negative labelling
11 Personalising and blaming

These thought patterns can be changed. The process to do this involves identifying our negative thoughts and changing them round to more positive ways of thinking. This process will help to reduce our levels of stress and also help us feel less negative about ourselves and our situations. We have provided you with a very structured technique for doing this analysis of your thoughts.

Further reading

A very readable and easy-to-follow guide to cognitive reassessment. Includes many examples and useful materials for the reader to use.

Burns, D. (1990) *Feeling Good: The New Mood Therapy*. New York: Simon and Schuster.

A good guide to techniques of dealing with patients, which includes some information about cognitive reassessment and more general methods of coping with stress.

Kent, G.G. and Blinkhorn, A.S. (1991) *The Psychology of Dental Care.* Oxford: Wright.

A useful guide to addressing the emotional stress of working in health professions.

Bailey, R.D. (1985) *Coping with Stress in Caring.* London: Blackwell Scientific Publications.

An article outlining many sources of stress faced by young general dental practitioners. Conflict between the time demands of practice and the GDP's personal perfectionism emerges as a source of tension for the majority of those surveyed.

Goodwin, W.C., Starks, D., Green, T. and Koran, A. 'Identification of sources of stress in practice by recent graduates'. *Journal of Education*, **45**: 220–1 (1981).

11

Am I still stressed?

In this chapter we have given you a second set of questionnaires for you to complete. This information will show you any changes in your stress levels since the last time you made these assessments. This will then allow you to plan how to change the levels of stress that remain. You can repeat these assessments as often as you like, but we would advise that you only complete these scales every six months, as any shorter period than that does not really give sufficient time for change.

What makes me feel stressed?

Make a list of everything in your work life that gives you the feeling of being stressed. You might want to draw on the examples we gave you in chapter 2, and see whether those apply to you personally.

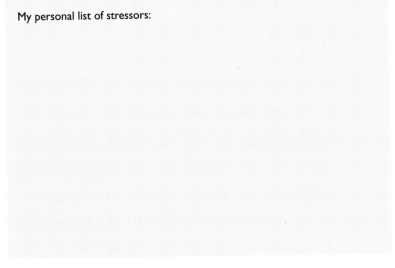

My personal list of stressors:

Fig 11.1a   Personal list of stressors

My personal TOP FIVE sources of stress

Importance Rank	Stress	Ease of Change
1		
2		
3		
4		
5		

Fig 11.1b   Top five sources of stress

1 Rank order your stressors and put them in the table (Figure 11.1b).
2 Rank each stress in terms of how easy it is to change.
3 Compare the list you have now made with your most recent list.

Have any stressors dropped off the list? What is new? Can you identify why these changes (if any) have occurred? Some stressors may be related, and working on one may ease the stress of another. So some sources of stress may have disappeared without any action on your part.

About my body

How often in an average week do you experience the signs and symptoms listed in Figure 11.2 at any time when you are travelling to work, at work, or when thinking about work?

Add up the score that you have given yourself.

If your score is 7 or below: You do not have many physiological signs and symptoms at this time. You should complete the other sections of this assessment, since it is possible that your personal stress is manifest in a different way. Ask those who work with you, and your close friends and family, whether they think you are experiencing stress. It may be that you simply have not noticed the signs.

| If your score is between 8 and 11: | You have distressing physiological signs and symptoms of stress. Chapters 5 and 10 will help you to identify ways to address these symptoms. |
| If your score is 12 or more: | This is a very high level of physiological symptoms, suggesting that you are having some signs at least twice a week, and possibly more often than this. Start with Chapter 5 and work through to looking at what makes your work environment so stressful (Chapter 6). |

| | Once a day or more | 2–3 times a week | Once a week or less |
	(Score 3)	(Score 2)	(Score 1)
Feeling that your heart is pounding			
Feeling that your pulse is racing			
Excessively sweaty hands			
'Butterflies' in the stomach			
Feeling that you are having difficulty breathing			
Feelings of muscle tension			
My total is: _____ Date: _____			

Fig. 11.2   Physiological signs and symptoms of stress

About my thoughts

How often in an average week do you experience the signs and symptoms listed in Figure 11.3?

Add up your score on the items (remembering to double your score on some items).

| If your score is 15 or less: | Your score is low. You rarely think negatively about your work situation. This is good. |

	Once a day or more (Score 3)	2–3 times a week (Score 2)	Once a week or less (Score 1)
Having difficulty concentrating			
Forgetting things, particularly little details			
Worrying about mistakes that you have made			
Worrying about what patients think of you			
Worrying about what your colleagues think of you			
Going over and over in your mind things that happened at work			
Having difficulty making decisions			
Losing confidence in yourself *			
Thinking of yourself as worthless *			
Feeling unhappy and depressed *			

* Score yourself double on these items

My total is: _____   Date: _____

Fig. 11.3   Cognitive signs and symptoms of stress

You should continue completing the questionnaires in this section, in case your stress is manifest in a different way.

If your score is between 16 and 25:

You experience quite a number of negative thoughts in relation to work. You should certainly consider reading Chapter 10 to identify how you might take a more positive attitude towards work and your work stress.

If your score is 26 or more:

You frequently think negatively about your work. You are probably approaching the limits of your stress. This high score is particularly concerning if you have indicated a very frequent response for the items marked with an asterisk. You should read Chapter 10 as a priority.

About my behaviour

Over the last six months have you noticed any of the following changes in behaviour?

	✓ or **x**
Smoking more	
Drinking more alcohol	
Changes in diet (eating more, eating less)	
Seeing less of friends	
Taking sick leave from work	
Having more arguments with colleagues	
Working late more often	
Missing more lunch breaks	
Number of changes identified: _____ Date: _____	

Fig. 11.4 Behavioural signs and symptoms of stress

If you have noticed any of the changes in behaviour listed in Figure 11.4 then we would advise you to read Chapter 9, which examines the effects of stress on behaviour, and Chapter 5, which will help you to find other ways of dealing with the effects of stress. The more of these changes that you have ticked, the more priority you should give to reading and working through Chapter 9.

About my health

Over the last six months have any of the aspects of your health listed in Figure 11.5 changed?

	✓ or x
Feelings of tiredness and fatigue	
Increased number of headaches and migraines	
Increased number of colds	
Increasing indigestion	
Feelings of low self-esteem	
Feeling anxious	
Feeling depressed	
Number of changes identified: _____ Date: _____	

Fig. 11.5   Effects of stress on health

The changes in health noted in Figure 11.5 are all to be taken seriously. If you are experiencing any of these changes we advise you to discuss them with a general medical practitioner. Chapter 5 is a good place to start, and will help you to identify ways to relax and take your mind off stress. Chapter 6 will help to identify any aspects of your physical environment which may be unhealthy. Chapters 7, 9 and 10 will all help you to identify new ways of dealing with your stress.

General questions

Overall how would you rate the level of stress that you are experiencing?
(Please circle one answer)

Low						High
1	2	3	4	5	6	7

How much do you want to change this level?
(Please circle one answer)

Not at all						Very high priority
1	2	3	4	5	6	7

Fig. 11.6   General questions

It is important that you consider your own willingness to change. If this is low then any help that is offered is likely to be unsuccessful.

Supplementary questions

The questions in Figure 11.7 are about how the stress you are experiencing affects those around you. They are for friends and colleagues to complete.

The perspectives of other people can be a useful guide to help you to decide to change your stress levels. Often our stress does not affect us but has quite a major impact on those around us. Compare your own willingness to change with how much those around you would like you to change your stress.

Ask a colleague at work:

What do you think is my stress level?
(Please circle one answer)
Low   High
    1   2   3   4   5   6   7

How much would you like me to change my stress levels?
(Please circle one answer)
Not at all   Very high priority
    1   2   3   4   5   6   7

Ask a close family member (your partner or another close relative):

What do you think is my stress level?
(Please circle one answer)
Low   High
    1   2   3   4   5   6   7

How much would you like me to change my stress levels?
(Please circle one answer)
Not at all   Very high priority
    1   2   3   4   5   6   7

Fig. 11.7 Supplementary questions

12

Summary

Our approach to modifying our experience to stress involves a cycle of change as outlined in Figure 12.1.

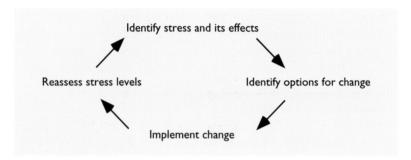

Fig. 12.1 Stress management cycle of change

Identify stress and its effects

We started our learning about stress by looking at what causes us to feel stressed and how stress affects our lives and outlined a model which suggested that stress is an *interaction* between the demand placed upon us and our ability to meet that demand. Any mismatch between ability and demand results in the harmful effects of stress. The effects of stress can be categorised into four broad groups. Stress affects our:

1 Physiology
2 Thoughts
3 Behaviour
4 Health

We then presented some questionnaires which assessed your current state in regard to stress. Your answers to these questions helped to ascertain areas in your life which needed change, and the priorities for change. These questionnaires help you to answer the question, 'Where am I now?' This is the important first step in identifying change.

Identify options for change and implement change

Having identified the level of stress that we are facing, and the sources of stress in our lives we then outlined a series of techniques for modifying stress levels. These techniques are outlined in Chapters 5 to 10. Each chapter takes a particular aspect of the dental environment and your role as a dental health professional and gives specific techniques for modifying that particular source of stress. Chapters 5 to 10 cover:

- Changing your lifestyle to minimise stress
- Changing the stressful environment
- Managing time
- Managing personnel
- Changing stress-related behaviour
- Changing stress-related thoughts

We recommend that you concentrate on learning and adopting one set of techniques at a time. Think of each as new skills that you can use to improve your quality of life, in much the same way as you might use new dental techniques to improve your treatments for patients.

Reassess stress levels

Finally, after undertaking any change it is important to re-evaluate the situation. This allows us to determine not only the extent to which improvements have been made, but also whether any further changes are necessary. We have enclosed a second set of questionnaires for you to use when assessing change. You may wish to keep a copy of these question-naires so that at a future date you can assess your stress.

In this book we hope you will have learned about stress and how it affects you personally as well as those you work with and those who are closest to you. We hope that you have found new ways of coping with and thinking about stress and that these will be invaluable in your profes-sional life.

Appendix
Useful addresses

This is not intended to be a comprehensive list but is an initial reference source.

BRITISH DENTAL ASSOCIATION

Useful source of information and guidance. The BDA will also be able to tell you about local groups in your area for support from colleagues.

British Dental Association
64 Wimpole Street
London
W1M 8AL   Telephone: 0171 935 0875

ALCOHOL AND DRUGS

For confidential information about problems with alcohol and drugs.

Health Information First
Level 2
Lister Hospital
Coreys Mill Lane
Stevenage
SG1 4AB   Telephone: 0800 665544

The Sick Dentists Scheme provides information and support for dentists who are experiencing problems with alcohol or drugs. The scheme can be contacted through the British Dental Association.

Sick Dentists Scheme
c/o British Dental Association
64 Wimpole Street
London
W1M 8AL   Telephone: 0171 487 3119

ALEXANDER TECHNIQUE

A technique which teaches how to change old postural habits and learn new ones. It is highly effective in treating and avoiding back complaints. For more information contact:

The Society of Teachers of the Alexander Technique
20 London House
266 Fulham Road
London
SW10 9EL   Telephone: 0171 351 0828

CHIROPRACTIC

Many people report that chiropractic techniques are useful in cases of back pain. To find a practitioner in your area contact:

The British Chiropractic Association
Premier House
10 Greycoat Place
London
SW1P ISB   Telephone: 0171 222 8866

COUNSELLING

Counselling provides a safe and non-judgmental setting in which to explore the stress you are experiencing. It is particularly useful if particular events or circumstances are causing worry or concern. If you or a colleague would like to find a counsellor in your area contact the British Association for Counselling who will be able to give you a list of registered counsellors in your area.

The British Association for Counselling
1 Regent Place
Rugby
CV21 2PJ   Telephone: 01788 578328

HEALTH EDUCATION AUTHORITY

The HEA can provide information on healthy eating, exercise and healthy behaviour (for example help with giving up smoking and cutting down on alcohol intake).

The Health Education Authority
Trevelyan House
30 Great Peter Street
London
SW1P 2HW   Telephone: 0171 222 5300

MEDITATION

In Chapter 5 we discussed techniques of relaxation and their value in managing stress. Meditation is a very deep form of relaxation.

Transcendental Meditation
FREEPOST
London
SW1P 4YY   Telephone: 0800 269303

OPEN UNIVERSITY

The Open University runs courses on management and other aspects of personal development. You may want to think about developing an interest outside your work, or developing skills which would be useful in your work.

Open University
Reservation
P O Box 724
Milton Keynes
MK7 6XS   Telephone: 01908 653231

APPENDIX **87**

OSTEOPATHY

For those who suffer aches and pains in their back or neck, osteopathy can provide relief. To find out about registered osteopaths in your area contact:

The General Council and Register of Osteopaths
56 London Street
Reading
Berkshire
RG1 4SQ   Telephone: 0118 957 6585

SHIATSU

Shiatsu is a form of massage which is very relaxing and has benefits for both body and mind. The Shiatsu Society UK can tell you of practitioners in your area.

The Shiatsu Society UK
Barber House
Storeys Bar Road
Fengate
Peterborough
PE1 5YS   Telephone: 01733 758341

SPORTS

Sports are relaxing, can be a form of social contact and help to keep you fit. For information about sporting activities in your area contact:

The Sports Council
16 Upper Woburn Place
London
WC1H 0QP   Telephone: 0171 273 1500

YOGA

Another form of relaxation is Yoga. It can also help to improve posture and so avoid strain on the back and neck. For information on courses contact:

The British Wheel of Yoga
1 Hamilton Place
Boston Road
Sleaford
Lincolnshire
NG34 7ES   Telephone: 01529 306851

Index

Absence, staff, 21
Acute (short-term) physiological
    effects of stress, 14–15, 22
Adaptation, response to stress, 6
Adrenaline, 14, 15, 30
Alarm, response to stress, 6
Alcohol consumption
    cutting down, 58
    increased due to stress, 18, 20
Alexander technique, 39
Alternative behaviours, 60–61, 62
Anxiety, 20
Appointing staff, 51
Arousal, increased due to stress,
    30
Autonomic nervous system
    (ANS), 14

Back problems, 20, 38–39
Barriers
    to changing behaviour, 60–61
    to relaxation training, 32
Basal Metabolic Rate, raised, 34
Behaviour
    changing, 57–64
    decreased repertoire, 18–19,
        59–61
    effects of stress on, 6, 7, 12,
        18–19, 22, 57–59
    self-assessment of changes, 27,
        79

Behavioural Analysis of Stress
    Events (BASE), 60, 62, 65
Black and white thinking, 67–68
Blaming, 69–70
Blinkhorn, A.S., 9
Blood pressure, 33–34
British Association for
    Counselling, 63
British Dental Association, 37, 38
Burns, D., 66
'Butterflies', 14

Caffeine, 32, 33–34
Catastrophising, 17
Challenge, 9
Change
    cycle of, 82–83
    lifestyle, 30–36
    willingness to, 80
    See also Behaviour
Chronic (long-term) physiological
    effects of stress, 14, 15, 22
Cognitive effects of stress, 7
    See also Thoughts
Cognitive reassessment, 66–73
Cognitive restructuring exercises,
    63
    See also Critical Analysis of
        Stress Events
Colds/flu, and stress, 20
Collapse, 6, 15

89

Communication
    effects of stress on, 20–21
    with team, 51–52, 54
Compromise, 68
Concentration, poor, 16
Control, lack of, 9–10, 47, 55
Controllable/uncontrollable
    stress, 8–9, 11, 12
Convenience/fast foods, 32, 33
Cooper, C.L., 11, 41, 61
Coping behaviour repertoire,
    decreased, 18–19, 59–61,
    64
Coping strategies, 60
Corticosteroids, 6, 15, 20
Cox, T., 7
Cox's Interactionist model of
    stress, 7
Critical Analysis of Stress Events
    (CASE), 70, 71, 72
Critical incidents, 64
    recognising impact, 61
    reviewing, 63
    and stress, 61, 63, 68
    support, 61, 62

'Dashers'. *See* 'Strollers/dashers'
Delegation, 47, 49
Demand and ability balance, 7–8,
    12, 19
Dental nurses
    sources of stress, 10
    and stress, 9–10
Dental surgeries, design, 37
Dentistry, sources of stress, 9–12
Dentists
    and back problems, 20, 38–39
    as businessmen, 11
    and hobbies, 34–35
    holidays, 47
    sources of stress, 11–12

Depression, 20
Diet
    effects of stress on, 18, 20
    healthy, 33, 59
    regular eating, 33
    to combat stress, 32–34, 36
'Diseases of adaptation', 6

Ears, stress and strain on, 37–38
Emotional reasoning, 69
Encouragement, 54
Environmental management,
    37–40
Exercise
    effect of stress on, 20
    to combat stress, 34, 36, 59
Exercises, stretching, 39
Exhaustion, response to stress, 6
Expectations of failure, 16
Eyes, stress and strain on, 37, 38

'Fight or flight', 5, 6, 14
Flexibility, decreased, 19

Global negative thoughts, 16–17
Goals, 45–46
    allocating time to, 46, 50
    prioritising, 46, 49, 50
Godwin, W.C., 67

Headaches/migraines, due to
    stress, 20
Health
    changes due to stress, 19–20,
    22, 64
    self-assessment, 28, 79–80
Health related behaviour, and
    stress, 57–59
Heart problems, due to long-term
    stress, 15, 20
Heart rate, increased, 14–15, 30

Hobbies, to combat stress, 34–35
Holmes and Rahe Schedule of
    Recent Events, 4, 5
Hygienists, sources of stress,
    10–11

Illness, through stress, 5, 19–20
Immune coping response,
    depleted, 20
Information, needed by dentist,
    48
Interactionist models of stress,
    7–9
Interruptions, 48
Intrusive negative thoughts, 16–17

'Jumping to conclusions', 69

Life change events, and stress, 4, 5
Lighting, 38, 40
Listening, importance of, 52

Magnification, 8, 17, 69
Meetings, 48
Memory loss, 16
Models of stress, 3–9
Motivation, effect of stress on, 21

Negative labelling, 69
Negative thinking, 8, 15–16,
    66–70
    catastrophising, 17
    categories of, 66
    magnification, 8, 17, 69
    rumination, 17
Noise, 37–38

Overgeneralisation, 68

Paperwork, 48
Pareto principle, 46

Part-time staff, needs of, 10
Patients, difficult, 11, 12, 68–69
Perceptions of demand, 8
Perfectionism, 67
Personalisation, 69–70
Personnel management, to
    minimise stress, 51–56
Physiological effects of stress,
    5–6, 7, 12, 14–15, 19–20,
    22, 25, 30
    self-assessment, 24–26, 76–77
Positive events, and stress, 5
Positive thinking, 18
Practical support, 35
Practice philosophy, 47, 49, 50
Predictable/unpredictable stress,
    8–9, 11, 12
Priorities, 41–43, 45–46, 49
Professional support networks, 35
Progressive muscular relaxation,
    30, 31
Pupils, widening, 30

Questionnaires, 23–29, 65, 75–81

Relaxation training, 30–32, 36
Response based models of stress,
    5–6, 7
Responsibility without control, 10
Rigidity of behaviour, 19
Role ambiguity, 21
Rosenman and Friedman, 44
Rumination, 17
'Rust out', 8

Schedule of Recent Events
    (Holmes and Rahe), 4, 5
Scheduling pressures, 41
Seating position (dentists), 38, 39
Selective focus, 68–69
Self-confidence, 8

Self-esteem, low, 20
Selye's General Adaptation
     Syndrome, 6, 15
'Shoulds', tyranny of, 67
Skeleton, strain on, 38, 39
Smoking
     giving up, 58
     increased, 18, 20, 57–58
Social support, 35, 36
Social withdrawal, 18–19
Stable negative thoughts, 16–17
Stimulus, different responses to, 5
Stimulus based models of stress,
     3–5, 6
Strengths and weaknesses,
     identifying own, 52
Stress
     audit, 23–29, 75–81
     definition, 3, 5, 7
     long term, 5, 14, 15, 22
     manifestations, 22
     physiological changes, 5–6
     reducing, 15
     as stimulus/force, 3
     See also Models of stress
Stressors
     environment free from, 37
     self-assessment, 23–24, 75–76
'Strollers/dashers', 44–45, 49
     effect on others, 45
Support, emotional, 35
Sweaty palms, 14

Team, forming, 51, 53
Team working, 20–21, 51–55
     commitment to objectives, 54

dependency, 52–54
feedback, 54, 55
meetings, 54
problems/conflict, 54–55
trust, 55
Telephone calls, 48
Thoughts
     changing, 70–73
     critical analysis, 70–73
     effects of stress on, 6, 12,
          15–18, 22
     self-assessment of effects of
          stress, 26–27, 77–79
     See also Cognitive reassessment
Time
     awareness of, 43
     constraints, 45–49
     external demands, 46–49
     priorities, 41–43
Time management, 41–50
     planning, 45–46
     time use diagrams, 42
     See also 'Strollers/dashers'
'Time stealers', 48
Turnover of staff, 21

Undervaluation of staff, 10

Waddington, T.J., 11, 12
Warren and Toll, 44
Work environment, handling
     change, 55
Work/leisure balance, 41, 42
Working relationships
     effects of stress on, 20–21, 22
     self assessment, 29, 81